Plain English Series:

Capitalization

by Kathleen Knoblock

**illustrated by
Renée Yates**

FS-10172 Plain English Series: Capitalization
All rights reserved–Printed in the U.S.A.
Copyright © 1995 Frank Schaffer Publications, Inc.
23740 Hawthorne Blvd.
Torrance, CA 90505

Plain English is a no-nonsense series designed to be used with students aged nine through adult who need instruction or reinforcement in basic English communication. *Capitalization* contains a selection of 11 skills common in everyday writing, but often confused or misused.

Table of Contents

Flow Chart

A flow chart is a useful tool for organizing your teaching and helping ensure that students reach skill mastery. The chart below outlines an effective approach for teaching the skills in this book using the materials provided.

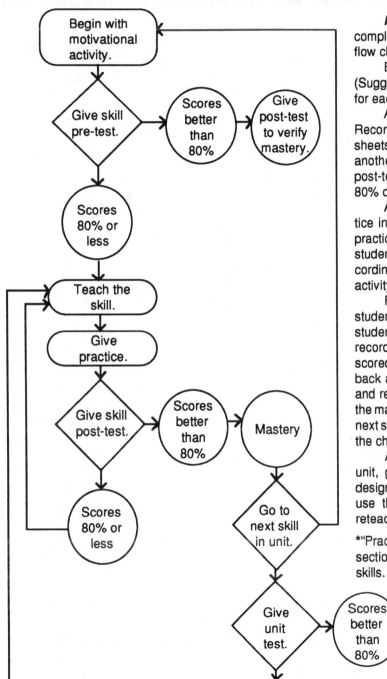

Plain English—Capitalization contains a complete 11-skill unit. Follow the steps in this flow chart to teach the skills in the unit.

Begin a lesson with a motivational activity. (Suggestions are given on the teaching pages for each skill.)

After introducing the skill, give the pre-test. Record the results on students' individual record sheets. If a student scores better than 80% (or another mastery level that you choose), give the post-test to verify mastery. If a student scores 80% or less, proceed to teach the skill.*

After direct instruction, give students practice in applying the skill. This book contains a practice sheet for each skill which can be done by students working together or individually. Recording the scores on the record sheet for this activity is optional.

Following instruction and practice, give students the post-test. Record the results on students' individual record sheets. Using the record sheets, form a group of students who scored 80% or less on the post-test; then go back and reteach the skill. Give more practice and repeat the post-test. When students reach the mastery level on the post-test, proceed to the next skill in the unit, beginning again at the top of the chart.

After teaching each of the 11 skills in the unit, give students the unit test. This test is designed to assess mastery in context. Again, use the test results to group students; then reteach any skills not yet mastered.

*"Practice With a Purpose" (pages 73–94) is a section of mini-charts that correspond with the skills. Use these versatile pages to teach, reteach, and provide additional practice and follow-up for each skill. Make transparencies from them, use them as file folder centers, reproduce them to make individual student rule/ practice books, or copy the exercises onto chart paper for group work.

Teachers often face the frustrating problem of having some students who have mastered a skill before it is taught, others who learn it from direct instruction, and still others who require reteaching and review. Here are some classroom-tested ideas for dealing with this problem. These ideas will help ensure that all students get the instruction they need, simplify your record keeping, and increase your accountability.

Terrific Teaching Tips

Teaching "By the Numbers"

Have each student keep an individual record sheet (page 95).

Tip! Assign each student a student number. An easy way to do this is to go in order down your class list. Have students put their numbers as well as their names on all work.

Tip! Each time an assessment is made, sort the students by number to group for teaching. For example, assume you have 30 students numbered 1–30. You have given the pre-test for a skill. (If your students can record their scores themselves, have them do it!) You know you will have to teach the skill to some, but probably not all, of your students. Quickly sort through the assessment papers, removing all those with scores better than 80% (or another mastery level that you have chosen). You now have two sets of papers. In your plan book jot down the numbers of the students who need direct instruction.

Tip! Copy only the number of practice pages needed. (This will save time and resources by eliminating the duplicating of unnecessary pages.) When you are ready to teach the skill, call out the numbers of those students who are to join the instructional group.

Cozy Clusters

After the directed lesson and practice, give the post-test to all students. Repeat the sorting process when planning a reteaching lesson. Again, prepare materials only for students who need them. Record keeping is simplified further because in your previous sorting you already separated the record sheets of those students.

Another way to group for instruction is to give several or all of the pre-tests before beginning any formal instruction. Then, sort the completed record sheets by skill mastery and teach skills in clusters. Perhaps you have students who have mastered most or all of the skills. Check by giving these students the unit test.

Skill Growth Portfolio

Help students take pride in their achievements and instill in them a greater sense of responsibility by having them create a skill growth portfolio in which they keep their tests, practice papers, and record sheets. This not only relieves you of that duty, but allows students to track their own progress and be more actively involved in their own learning.

Tip! Have students make their own rule books to keep in their portfolios as they work through the skills. (See idea below.) Have students copy the rules as you teach them or use the "Practice With a Purpose" mini-charts in one of the ways described below.

"Practice With a Purpose" Mini-charts

"Practice With a Purpose" is a special section of mini-charts designed to provide extra opportunities to extend and reinforce skills. It includes a ready-to-use rule page for lessons and reference, plus a practice page for application and follow-up for each skill. First, a "rule of thumb" is given in simple language along with correct (✓) and incorrect (✗) examples. Then, the practice page provides an additional opportunity to apply the skill in context. Here are a few ways to use these special pages.

• Overhead Transparencies and Charts

Copy the rules and/or practice activity onto chart paper for small group instruction. After the lesson, post the chart as a reference for students.

Make a set of rule and practice transparencies directly from the pages. Use the rule transparency to teach or reteach the skill. Then use the practice transparency to have students record on paper their responses to the exercises on the overhead screen. Correct the activity together. After marking the answers in grease pencil, simply wipe the transparency clean and it is ready to use again.

• Rule and Practice File Folder Centers

Make a photocopy of each skill's rule and practice pages. Mount the copies side-by-side in a file folder. Write the skill on the tab. These folders can be posted or placed in a box for students to complete independently.

• Individual Student Rule and Practice Books

Have students copy rules from charts, transparencies, or file folders to make their own rule books. The following page provides a reproducible rule book template (with space for students to write the rule and practice answers). Or, reproduce the rule and practice pages directly for students to compile into books.

Capitalization—By the Rules

Name _____ **Date** _____

Skill _____

_____

_____

_____

_____

_____

_____

_____

_____

Rule of Thumb

Examples

✗ _____

✓ _____

✗ _____

✓ _____

Practice

1. _____

2. _____

3. _____

4. _____

5. _____

Related materials for teaching Capitalization: Pronoun—*I*
Reproducible: Pre-test and Post-test (page 12); Practice Page (page 11)
Enrichment Activity (page 10)
Rule Book Template (page 6); Individual Record Sheet (page 95)
"Practice With a Purpose": Pronoun—*I* (pages 73-74)

Capitalization: Pronoun—*I*

The ideas on these three pages follow the flow chart of suggested steps for teaching, reteaching, and testing presented on page 3 of this book.

STEP 1:
Motivation—By Myself

The most basic of capitalization rules is that regarding capitalization of the pronoun *I*. Assess your students' awareness of this rule by presenting the following sentences or other examples in which the pronoun *I* is shown in lowercase. Without discussing what errors to look for, ask students to write each sentence correctly.

- Lois and i are homework buddies.
- i need help with math, so she helps me.
- She needs help with spelling, so i help her.
- Mom thinks Lois and i have a good system.
- Lois agrees, and so do i.

STEP 2:
Pre-test and Grouping for Instruction

Some of your students may overlook capitalizing the pronoun *I* when writing sentences. Follow the introduction above by giving all students the written pre-test (page 12). Record (or have students record) their scores on an individual record sheet (page 95). Sort through the record sheets and remove the tests of students who scored 100%. You may choose to give these students the post-test right away to verify mastery or wait to give it to them with the rest of the class. Form a group of students who scored 80% or lower for direct instruction and practice.

STEP 3:
Instruction

Begin the lesson by having students compare the corrected sentences below with their own corrected sentences.

Explain to students that a pronoun is a word that takes the place of a noun. Have several volunteers read each sentence, substituting their own name for every *I*. Ask students what the pronoun *I* refers to in each sentence. Explain to students that since it sounds odd for a person to call himself or herself by name, the pronoun *I* is used to take the place of the person's own name.

• Lois and *I* are homework buddies.
• *I* need help with math, so she helps me.
• She needs help with spelling, so *I* help her.
• Mom thinks Lois and *I* have a good system.
• Lois agrees, and so do *I*.

Next, present sentences containing the contractions *I'll, I'm,* and *I'd.* Ask students what each contraction means and why it is capitalized.

• I'll meet you there. (I will)
• I'm going to be late. (I am)
• I'd better call first. (I had)
• I'd like to get a good seat. (I would)

Finally, have students suggest a general rule for writing the pronoun *I*. (If you are using "Practice With a Purpose" coordinated mini-charts, use the rule page with this lesson.)

RULE 1 👉 **Always capitalize the pronoun *I*.**

✓ Don and *I* went home.

NOTE! Contractions beginning with the pronoun *I* are also capitalized.

✓ *I'll* meet you there.
   (*I* will)
✓ *I'm* going to be late.
   (*I* am)
✓ *I'd* better call first.
   (*I* had)
✓ *I'd* like to get a good seat.
   (*I* would)

STEP 4:
Apply and Practice

Following direct instruction, give students the opportunity to apply the skill in practice. You may use the prepared practice sheet provided (page 11), side two of the "Practice With a Purpose" mini-chart (page 74), or your own practice sentences. Students can use plain writing paper to copy and correct sentences you write on the board or those provided on the mini-chart. If you choose to use the reproducible practice sheet, duplicate only the number needed for your instructional group. (Use the pre-test results to determine the exact number of students who will need practice.)

Practice may be guided or done independently. Students may work individually, in pairs, or as a group. Correct the page together or privately to assess the need for reteaching before giving the post-test.

STEP 5:
Post-test and Reteaching

When your students have had sufficient instruction and practice, give the post-test. After recording scores on the individual record sheets, once again separate the sheets of those students who scored 80% or less on the post-test for reteaching. You may use or reuse any of the materials suggested in Step 4 for reteaching.

Follow-up / Enrichment

Once students have mastered the skill, make certain they retain it by giving a follow-up activity several weeks later. An excellent way to do this is to see if they can apply the skill in context. Below is a riddle you can copy onto chart paper to check for retention. Have students rewrite the riddle correctly. Or, if you prefer, use the prepared reproducible activity sheet on the following page. **Tip!** Let students draw the answer to the riddle (a railroad).

To be corrected

What Am I?

i've been around for more than 200 years. Sometimes i carry people, and at other times i am used to transport freight or mail. i have cars, but i do not travel on roads. Although i am not an animal, my nickname is "iron horse." What am i?

Corrected

What Am I?

I've been around for more than 200 years. Sometimes I carry people, and at other times I am used to transport freight or mail. I have cars, but I do not travel on roads. Although I am not an animal, my nickname is "iron horse." What am I?

ANSWER KEYS

Pre-test:

1. A) correct
2. B) I
3. B) I
4. A) correct
5. B) I

Practice:

1. A) correct
2. B) I'd
3. B) I
4. A) correct
5. B) I

6. A) correct
7. B) I've
8. A) correct
9. B) I'm
10. B) I

Post-test:

1. B) I
2. B) I'd
3. A) correct
4. B) I
5. A) correct

**Practice With a Purpose—
  Pronoun—*I***

1. Dad and I . . .
2. I haven't . . .
3. Dad says I . . .

4. If I wait . . .
5. When I do . . .   I'll throw it . . .

Pronoun—*I*

Read the riddle. Use the capitalization rule you have learned for the pronoun *I* to circle each error you see. Copy the riddle correctly on the lines. In the box, draw the answer to the riddle.

What Am I?

    i've been around for more than 200 years. Sometimes i carry people, and at other times i am used to transport freight or mail. i have cars, but i do not travel on roads. Although i am not an animal, my nickname is "iron horse." What am i?

_____

_____

_____

_____

_____

_____

_____

Prounoun—I

Directions: Read carefully. Circle *A* if there is no capitalization error. Circle *B* if the change indicated is needed.

A Bear, a Bee, or Me?

(1) If I were a big brown bear,   A) correct   B) i

(2) A cave i'd call my home.   A) correct   B) I'd

(3) Sweet honey i would find in hives,   A) correct   B) I

(4) As through the woods I'd roam.   A) correct   B) i'd

(5) But if i were a honeybee,   A) correct   B) I

(6) I wouldn't like that bear.   A) correct   B) i

(7) For once i've made my honeycombs,   A) correct   B) I've

(8) I wouldn't want to share!   A) correct   B) i

(9) So I'm glad i'm NOT a bear or bee—   A) correct   B) I'm

(10) i am better off just being me.   A) correct   B) I

Name _____ **Date** _____ **Score** _____

Prounoun—*I*

Directions: Read carefully. Circle *A* if there is no capitalization error. Circle *B* if the change indicated is needed.

1. Yesterday I made a rug for my cat.   A) correct   B) i

2. i saw the directions in a craft magazine.   A) correct   B) I

3. First i tore strips of cloth; then I braided them.   A) correct   B) I

4. To shape the rug, I sewed the braids together.   A) correct   B) i

5. The rug i made is called a rag rug.   A) correct   B) I

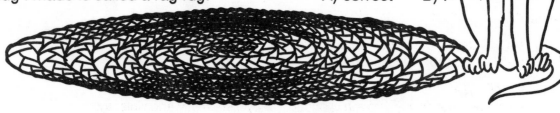

Name _____ **Date** _____ **Score** _____

Prounoun—*I*

Directions: Read carefully. Circle *A* if there is no capitalization error. Circle *B* if the change indicated is needed.

1. Someday i would like to own a ranch.
   A) correct   B) I

2. I think i'd enjoy riding my horse over many acres.
   A) correct   B) I'd

3. If I found a lost calf, I'd bring it home.
   A) correct   B) i'd

4. At night the ranch hands and i would make a campfire.
   A) correct   B) I

5. Then we would sing while I played the guitar.
   A) correct   B) i

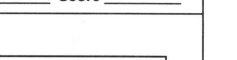

Related materials for teaching Capitalization: Beginning of a Sentence
Reproducible: Pre-test and Post-test (page 18); Practice Page (page 17)
Enrichment Activity (page 16)
Rule Book Template (page 6); Individual Record Sheet (page 95)
"Practice With a Purpose": Beginning of a Sentence (pages 75-76)

Capitalization: Beginning of a Sentence

The ideas on these three pages follow the flow chart of suggested steps for teaching, reteaching, and testing presented on page 3 of this book.

STEP 1:

Motivation—Just the Beginning

Introduce the skill by writing several sentences in which you have left out the first letter of the initial word in the sentence and the first letters of a few random words within the sentences. Without discussing capitalization, ask students to copy the sentences and fill in the missing letters. Suggested sentences appear below.

_eep inside the earth the _emperature is hot enough to melt rock.

_his melted rock is called *magma*.

_eat and pressure can cause magma to make _ts way to the surface.

_t can seep out slowly through cracks or _scape suddenly and violently.

_agma that reaches the surface is called *lava*.

_olcanoes are _ormed by the build-up of cooling lava.

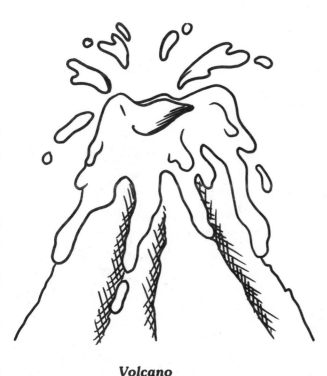

Volcano

STEP 2:

Pre-test and Grouping for Instruction

It is probable that some of your students have occasionally written sentences without capitalizing the first letter. Follow the introduction above by giving all students the written pre-test (page 18). Record (or have students record) their scores on an individual record sheet (page 95). Sort through the record sheets and remove the tests of students who scored 100%. You may choose to give these students the post-test right away to verify mastery or wait to give it to them with the rest of the class. Form a group of students who scored 80% or lower for direct instruction and practice.

STEP 3:
Instruction

Present students with the corrected sentences from the motivational activity. Ask students to compare their sentences with the corrected ones.

Deep inside the earth the **t**emperature is hot enough to melt rock.

This melted rock is called *magma*.

Heat and pressure can cause magma to make **I**ts way to the surface.

It can seep out slowly through cracks or **e**scape suddenly and violently.

Magma that reaches the surface is called *lava*.

Volcanoes are **f**ormed by the build-up of cooling lava.

Ask students to suggest a capitalization rule that can be applied to any sentence. (If you are using the "Practice With a Purpose" coordinated mini-charts, use the rule page with this lesson.)

RULE 1

Always capitalize the first word of a sentence.

✓ The word *volcano* is rooted in Roman mythology.

✓ **A** Roman god named Vulcan was believed to have lived deep within the earth.

✓ **W**hen Vulcan became angry, the myth claims, he spit fire out from below.

STEP 4:
Apply and Practice

Following direct instruction, give students the opportunity to apply the skill in practice. You may use the prepared practice sheet provided (page 17), side two of the "Practice With a Purpose" mini-chart (page 76), or your own practice sentences. Students can use plain writing paper to copy and correct sentences you write on the board or those provided on the mini-chart. If you choose to use the reproducible practice sheet, duplicate only the number needed for your instructional group. (Use the pre-test results to determine the exact number of students who will need practice.)

Practice may be guided or done independently. Students may work individually, in pairs, or as a group. Correct the page together or privately to assess the need for reteaching before giving the post-test.

STEP 5:
Post-test and Reteaching

When your students have had sufficient instruction and practice, give the post-test. After recording scores on the individual record sheets, once again separate the sheets of those students who scored 80% or less on the post-test for reteaching. You may use or reuse any of the materials suggested in Step 4 for reteaching.

Follow-up / Enrichment

Once students have mastered the skill, make certain they retain it by giving a follow-up activity several weeks later. An excellent way to do this is to see if they can apply the skill in context. To check for retention, copy the scrambled sentences at the right onto chart paper. Have students unscramble the sentences and write them correctly. (They will need to capitalize the first word of each sentence.) Or, if you prefer, use the prepared reproducible activity sheet on the following page. **Tip!** Invite pairs of students to create their own scrambled sentences to trade and unscramble.

To be corrected

Past Life
1. remains lived that ago plants are the and of fossils long animals.
2. type bones animal one of are fossil.
3. another fossil is of called type mold a.
4. impression plant animal left or by formed after a is a decays mold an.
5. useful fossils information years life scientists give about can of millions ago.

Corrected

Past Life
1. <u>F</u>ossils are the remains of plants and animals that lived long ago.
2. <u>A</u>nimal bones are one type of fossil.
3. <u>A</u>nother type of fossil is called a mold.
4. <u>A</u> mold is formed by an impression left after a plant or animal decays.
5. <u>F</u>ossils can give scientists useful information about life millions of years ago.

ANSWER KEYS

Pre-test:
1. **Almost** . . .
2. **Some** . . .
3. **Others** . . .
4. **Collections** . . .
5. **People** . . .

Practice:
1. A) **Can** . . .
2. A) **If** . . .
3. A) **No,** . . .
4. B) **the** . . .
5. B) **but** . . .
6. A) **Parrots** . . .
7. B) **In** . . .
8. A) **They** . . .
9. A) **That** . . .
10. B) **answer** . . .

Post-test:
1. **A** . . .
2. **His** . . .
3. **The** . . .
4. **Yes,** . . .
5. **From** . . .

**Practice With a Purpose—
Beginning of a Sentence**

1. **How** . . .
2. **The** . . .
3. **Meat-eaters** . . .
4. **Desert-dwelling** . . .
5. **Many** . . .

Beginning of a Sentence

The sentences below are scrambled. Rearrange the word order to make five sentences about fossils. Write the sentences on the lines. Capitalize words as needed.

Past Life

1. remains lived that ago plants are the and of fossils long animals.

_____

_____

_____

2. type bones animal one of are fossil.

_____

_____

_____

3. another fossil is of called type mold a.

_____

_____

_____

4. impression plant animal left or by formed after a is a decays mold an.

_____

_____

_____

5. useful fossils information years life scientists give about can of millions ago.

_____

_____

_____

Beginning of a Sentence

Directions: Read carefully. Circle the letter of the correct form of the word that belongs in each numbered blank.

No Secrets

___ you keep a secret? ___ not,
(1)   (2)

don't tell it to a parrot. ___, ___ parrot
(3)   (4)

will not understand what you say, ___
(5)

it may repeat it to someone that does!

___ have the ability to copy the sounds
(6)

of human speech ___ any language.
(7)

___ can even connect certain sounds
(8)

they hear with other sounds. ___ is
(9)

why parrots can be trained to "___"
(10)

questions or the telephone.

1. A) Can   B) can

2. A) If   B) if

3. A) No   B) no

4. A) The   B) the

5. A) But   B) but

6. A) Parrots B) parrots

7. A) In   B) in

8. A) They   B) they

9. A) That   B) that

10. A) Answer B) answer

Beginning of a Sentence

Directions: Read carefully. Fill in the missing letter at the beginning of each sentence.

1. __ lmost anything a person likes to do in his or her spare time can be a hobby.

2. __ome people enjoy sports, hiking, jogging, or other active hobbies.

3. __thers prefer handicrafts, painting, drawing, or writing.

4. __ollections are very popular, too.

5. __eople collect everything from antiques to insects!

Beginning of a Sentence

Directions: Read carefully. Fill in the missing letter at the beginning of each sentence.

1. __ famous person visited the White House in 1877 to demonstrate his invention.

2. __is name was Thomas A. Edison.

3. __he phonograph was the invention he proudly showed the president.

4. __es, you know Edison and his inventions, but do you know the name of the president he visited?

5. __rom 1877 to 1881, the president of the United States was Rutherford B. Hayes!

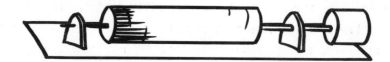

Related materials for teaching Capitalization: Beginning of a Quote
Reproducible: Pre-test and Post-test (page 24); Practice Page (page 23)
Enrichment Activity (page 22)
Rule Book Template (page 6); Individual Record Sheet (page 95)
"Practice With a Purpose": Beginning of a Quote (pages 77-78)

Capitalization: Beginning of a Quote

The ideas on these three pages follow the flow chart of suggested steps for teaching, reteaching, and testing presented on page 3 of this book.

STEP 1:
Motivation—In Their Own Words

Introduce the skill by recording the sentences below on a chart or on the chalkboard as shown (without capitalization in quotes). Ask three volunteers to take the parts of Nick, Janet, and the narrator and read the story aloud. Next, have students copy the sentences, and then underline the direct quotes. Finally, ask students to go back and change any lowercase letter that should be capitalized.

Nick and Janet were presenting to the class what they had learned about jellyfish.

"jellyfish," Janet said, "are not fish and they are not made of jelly."

Nick added, "they get their names from the jellylike material that forms their bodies."

"the jellylike dome," Janet continued, "is the main body. Hanging from the dome are a food tube and tentacles."

"have you ever wondered how a jellyfish swims?" asked Nick.

"i'll tell them, Nick," Janet answered. "it swims by opening and closing like an umbrella."

"yes," said Nick. "that is true whether the jellyfish is less than an inch in diameter or seven feet across!"

STEP 2:
Pre-test and Grouping for Instruction

Follow the introduction above by giving all students the written pre-test (page 24). Record (or have students record) their scores on an individual record sheet (page 95). Sort through the record sheets and remove the tests of students who scored 100%. You may choose to give these students the post-test right away to verify mastery or wait to give it to them with the rest of the class. Form a group of students who scored 80% or lower for direct instruction and practice.

STEP 3:
Instruction

Writing quotes correctly involves a number of complex capitalization and punctuation rules. This lesson covers only simple capitalization. Begin instruction by presenting the capitalization rule below. (If you are using the "Practice With a Purpose" coordinated mini-charts, use the rule page for this lesson.)

RULE 1 ☛ **Capitalize the first word of a sentence in a direct quote.**

HINT! Think of quotes as separate, complete sentences. If a quoted sentence is begun, interrupted, then continues, capitalize the beginning of the quote, but not the fragment that completes the sentence.

Use the motivational sentences to illustrate this rule. Correct them together. As you examine each quote, have students tell whether it is an uninterrupted complete sentence, or is interrupted and continues with a fragment. Challenge them to say how the capitalization rule applies.

Nick and Janet were presenting to the class what they had learned about jellyfish.

"Jellyfish," Janet said, "are not fish and they are not made of jelly." *(Quoted sentence is interrupted.)*

Nick added, "They get their names from the jellylike material that forms their bodies." *(Quote is a complete sentence.)*

"The jellylike dome," Janet continued, "is the main body. Hanging from the dome are a food tube and tentacles." *(Quoted sentence is interrupted.)*

"Have you ever wondered how a jellyfish swims?" asked Nick. *(Quote is a complete sentence.)*

"I'll tell them, Nick," Janet answered. "It swims by opening and closing like an umbrella." *(Each quote is a separate, complete sentence.)*

"Yes," said Nick. "That is true whether the jellyfish is less than an inch in diameter or seven feet across!" *(Each quote is a separate, complete sentence.)*

STEP 4:
Apply and Practice

Following direct instruction, give students the opportunity to apply the skill in practice. You may use the prepared practice sheet provided (page 23), side two of the "Practice With a Purpose" mini-chart (page 78), or your own practice sentences. Students can use plain writing paper to copy and correct sentences you write on the board or those provided on the mini-chart. If you choose to use the reproducible practice sheet, duplicate only the number needed for your instructional group. (Use the pre-test results to determine the exact number of students who will need practice.)

Practice may be guided or done independently. Students may work individually, in pairs, or as a group. Correct the page together or privately to assess the need for reteaching before giving the post-test.

STEP 5:
Post-test and Reteaching

When your students have had sufficient instruction and practice, give the post-test. After recording scores on the individual record sheets, once again separate the sheets of those students who scored 80% or less on the post-test for reteaching. Use or reuse any of the materials suggested in Step 4 for reteaching.

Follow-up / Enrichment

Once students have mastered the skill, make certain they retain it by giving a follow-up activity several weeks later. An excellent way to do this is to see if they can apply the skill in context. Use the story at the right to check for retention. Copy it onto chart paper or, if you prefer, use the prepared reproducible activity sheet on the following page. **Tip!** Let students use a stamp pad to make their fingerprints and then compare them.

To be corrected

Fingerprints

Carla asked the FBI agent who was visiting our class, "is it true that no two people have the same fingerprints?"

"yes," answered the agent. "fingerprints are unique."

"they all look alike to me," commented Mike. "what's the difference?"

"fingerprints fall into three main groups," the agent explained, "arches, loops, and whorls. But within each group there are infinite variations of the number and patterns of ridges."

Carla said, "so an exact fingerprint match is positive identification!"

Corrected

Fingerprints

Carla asked the FBI agent who was visiting our class, "Is it true that no two people have the same fingerprints?"

"Yes," answered the agent. "Fingerprints are unique."

"They all look alike to me," commented Mike. "What's the difference?"

"Fingerprints fall into three main groups," the agent explained, "arches, loops, and whorls. But within each group there are infinite variations of the number and patterns of ridges."

Carla said, "So an exact fingerprint match is positive identification!"

ANSWER KEYS

Pre-test:

1. B)	4. A)
2. B)	5. A)
3. B)	

Practice:

1. B)	5. A)	8. B)
2. B)	6. B)	9. B)
3. B)	7. B)	10. B)
4. B)		

Post-test:

1. B)	4. B)
2. A)	5. A)
3. B)	

**Practice With a Purpose—
Beginning of a Quote**

1. "**Did** you know," said Manuel, "**that** . . .
2. . . . replied, "**When** I think . . .
3. "**Actually**," . . . said Manuel. "**Even** moose . . .
4. . . . moment and then said, "**What** other . . .
5. . . . and laughed, "**What** about . . .

Beginning of a Quote

Use the rules you have learned for capitalizing quotes to find and circle in the story any lowercase letters that should be capital letters. Then copy the story correctly on the lines.

Fingerprints

Carla asked the FBI agent who was visiting our class, "is it true that no two people have the same fingerprints?"

"yes," answered the agent. "fingerprints are unique."

"they all look alike to me," commented Mike. "what's the difference?"

"fingerprints fall into three main groups," the agent explained, "arches, loops, and whorls. But within each group there are infinite variations of the number and patterns of ridges."

Carla said, "so an exact fingerprint match is positive identification!"

arch

loop

whorl

_____

_____

_____

_____

_____

_____

_____

_____

_____

_____

_____

_____

BONUS! Use a stamp pad to ink your finger. Put your fingerprint in the empty box. Examine your print. Is it an arch, a loop, or a whorl?

_____

Name _____   Date _____   Score _____

Beginning of a Quote

Directions: Read carefully. Write *A* if the **boldfaced** word is correct as is. Write *B* if it should be capitalized.

Dodo

_____ 1.   Mr. Sims asked, "**can** anyone name an extinct animal?"

_____ 2.   "I can," replied Anton. "**the** dodo bird is extinct."

_____ 3.   "**that's** right, Anton," said Mr. Sims. "The dodo died out about 1680."

_____ 4.   Karen added, "**dodos** couldn't fly."

_____ 5.   "Yes, but that's not why they died out," **said** Mr. Sims.

_____ 6.   "**why** did they, then?" asked Karen.

_____ 7.   "I think I know," said Anton. "**may** I answer?"

_____ 8.   Mr. Sims smiled and said, "**of** course."

_____ 9.   "The dodos lived on an island in the Indian Ocean," said Anton. "**seamen** came and ate the birds and introduced new animals that destroyed the eggs."

_____ 10.   "**yes**, that's true." said Mr. Sims sadly. "People sometimes throw off the balance of nature."

FS-10172 Plain English—Capitalization

Beginning of a Quote

Directions: Read carefully. Write *A* if the **boldfaced** word is correct as is. Write *B* if it should be capitalized.

_____ 1.   Mrs. Dean asked, "**where** is the lowest land area in America?"

_____ 2.   "I know," replied Carl. "**it** is in Death Valley."

_____ 3.   "**yes**," said Mrs. Dean. "The lowest point is 282 feet below sea level."

_____ 4.   "Where is Death Valley?" **asked** Susan.

_____ 5.   "It is in California," answered Mr. Sims, "**near** the Nevada border."

Beginning of a Quote

Directions: Read carefully. Write *A* if the **boldfaced** word is correct as is. Write *B* if it should be capitalized.

_____ 1.   Lisa asked, "**what** is the Leaning Tower of Pisa?"

_____ 2.   "It is a bell tower in Italy," **answered** her mother.

_____ 3.   "**does** it really lean?" Lisa asked.

_____ 4.   "Yes," replied her mother. "**in** fact, it looks as though it should fall over."

_____ 5.   "But the Tower of Pisa," Lisa's mother added with a smile, "**has** been leaning for over 600 years!"

Related materials for teaching Capitalization: People / Animals
Reproducible: Pre-test and Post-test (page 30); Practice Page (page 29)
Enrichment Activity (page 28)
Rule Book Template (page 6); Individual Record Sheet (page 95)
"Practice With a Purpose": People / Animals (pages 79-80)

Capitalization: People / Animals

The ideas on these three pages follow the flow chart of suggested steps for teaching, reteaching, and testing presented on page 3 of this book.

STEP 1:
Motivation—It Is Proper

Introduce the skill by writing several pairs of sentences that include the names of people, pets, and animal characters. (Do not capitalize the proper names.) Tell students to look for one or more capitalization errors in each sentence pair. Ask students to rewrite the sentences correctly. Here is a group of suggested sentences:

• Is that your horse, tasha?
• Yes, her name is velvet.

• My name is donnell jackson.
• My friends call me d. j.

• The speaker took questions from the audience.
• What do you think of the proposal, senator?

• Herman Melville wrote a book about a great whale.
• The whale's name was moby dick.

STEP 2:
Pre-test and Grouping for Instruction

Following the brief introduction above, give all students the written pre-test (page 30). Record (or have students record) their scores on an individual record sheet (page 95). Sort through the record sheets and remove the tests of students who scored 100%. You may choose to give these students the post-test right away to verify mastery or wait to give it to them with the rest of the class. Form a group of students who scored 80% or lower for direct instruction and practice.

STEP 3:
Instruction

Begin by presenting students with the two-part capitalization rule that follows. (If you are using "Practice With a Purpose" coordinated mini-charts, use the rule page for this lesson.)

RULE 1 **Capitalize names and initials of people.**

 **Capitalize names of pets and animal characters.**

> **HINT!** Names of specific people (such as *Pam* or *Dad*) and specific animal names (such as *Fluffy*) are capitalized. General names not referring to or addressing a specific individual (such as a *girl,* her *father,* and the *cat*) are not.

Illustrate the differences between specific names (proper nouns) and general names (common nouns) by correcting together and discussing the sentence pairs used in the motivational activity.

- Is that your horse, **Tasha**? *(specific person)*
- Yes, her name is **Velvet**. *(specific animal)*

- My name is **Donnell Jackson**. *(specific person)*
- My friends call me **D. J.** *(initials of a person)*

- The speaker took questions from the audience. *(general name)*
- What do you think of the proposal, **Senator**? *(specific name—the title* Senator *is used to address an individual in place of the individual's name)*

- Herman Melville wrote a book about a great whale. *(general name)*
- The whale's name was **Moby Dick**. *(specific animal)*

STEP 4:
Apply and Practice

Following direct instruction, give students the opportunity to apply the skill in practice. You may use the prepared practice sheet provided (page 29), side two of the "Practice With a Purpose" mini-chart (page 80), or your own practice sentences. Students can use plain writing paper to copy and correct sentences you write on the board or those provided on the mini-chart. If you choose to use the reproducible practice sheet, duplicate only the number needed for your instructional group. (Wait for the pre-test results to determine the exact number of students who will need practice.)

Practice may be guided or done independently. Students may work individually, in pairs, or as a group. Correct the page together or privately to assess the need for reteaching before giving the post-test.

STEP 5:
Post-test and Reteaching

When your students have had sufficient instruction and practice, give the post-test. After recording scores on the individual record sheets, once again separate the sheets of those students who scored 80% or less on the post-test for reteaching. You may use or reuse any of the materials suggested in Step 4 for reteaching.

Follow-up / Enrichment

Once students have mastered the skill, make certain they retain it by giving a follow-up activity several weeks later. An excellent way to do this is to see if they can apply the skill in context. To check for retention, you can copy the activity at the right onto chart paper; then ask students to follow the directions given. Or, if you prefer, use the prepared reproducible activity sheet on the following page. **Tip!** Invite students to read one of the books described.

To be corrected and completed

Book Match
Directions: Write each book description correctly. Then find and write the book title it describes: *Johnny Tremain, The Incredible Journey, Twenty Thousand Leagues Under the Sea, A Christmas Carol,* or *The Mouse and the Motorcycle.*
1. In this story by charles dickens, scrooge learns a lesson about life.
2. Three pets find their way through the wilderness in this book by sheila burnford.
3. A mouse named ralph is the star of this comic tale by beverly cleary.
4. In this story by esther forbes, the Revolutionary War touches the life of a young man named johnny.
5. Author jules verne included a submarine in this futuristic underwater adventure.

Corrected

Book Match
1. . . . **C**harles **D**ickens; **S**crooge / *A Christmas Carol*
2. . . . **S**heila **B**urnford / *The Incredible Journey*
3. . . . **R**alph; **B**everly **C**leary / *The Mouse and the Motorcycle*
4. . . . **E**sther **F**orbes; **J**ohnny / *Johnny Tremain*
5. . . . **J**ules **V**erne / *Twenty Thousand Leagues Under the Sea*

ANSWER KEYS

Pre-test:

1. B) Seurat
2. A) correct
3. C) Sophocles
4. C) Horse
5. B) B.

Practice:

1. C) Jones
2. A) correct
3. B) Tom
4. A) correct
5. C) Cricket

6. B) Johnson
7. C) Soros
8. A) correct
9. C) Tylers
10. A) correct

Post-test:

1. A) correct
2. B) Judy
3. B) P.J.
4. C) Steven
5. B) Mom

**Practice With a Purpose—
People / Animals**

1. E. B. White
2. Wilbur
3. Fern

4. Templeton
5. Wilbur's; Charlotte
   Charlotte's Web

People / Animals

Each book description below contains one or more errors in capitalization. First copy the description correctly. Then write the title of the book described.

The Mouse and the Motorcycle

Twenty Thousand Leagues Under the Sea

The Incredible Journey

Johnny Tremain

A Christmas Carol

Book Match

1. In this story by charles dickens, scrooge learns a lesson about life.

2. Three pets find their way through the wilderness in this book by sheila burnford.

3. A mouse named ralph is the star of this comic tale by beverly cleary.

4. In this story by esther forbes, the Revolutionary War touches the life of a young man named johnny.

5. Author jules verne included a submarine in this futuristic underwater adventure.

1. _____

_____

_____

2. _____

_____

_____

3. _____

_____

_____

4. _____

_____

_____

5. _____

_____

_____

People / Animals

Directions: For each sentence write *A* if no change is needed. Write *B* or *C* if the given word should be capitalized.

My Neighbors

_____ 1. My name is Sadie jones.
A) correct   B) Name   C) Jones

_____ 2. I live in an apartment building with many other families.
A) correct   B) Apartment   C) Building

_____ 3. In apartment 1-B are tom Denny and his wife Ann.
A) correct   B) Tom   C) Wife

_____ 4. Their son Joey is in my class at school.
A) correct   B) Class   C) School

_____ 5. Mrs. Adler lives in apartment 1-C with her cat, cricket.
A) correct   B) Cat   C) Cricket

_____ 6. The johnson family lives in apartment 1-D.
A) correct   B) Johnson   C) Family

_____ 7. Right above us in apartment 2-A are Neil and Michael soros.
A) correct   B) Above   C) Soros

_____ 8. Next to them lives a musician named Albert.
A) correct   B) Musician   C) Named

_____ 9. Albert's parents, the tylers, live in 2-C.
A) correct   B) Parents   C) Tylers

_____ 10. It is fun to have so many nice neighbors.
A) correct   B) Nice   C) Neighbors

Name _____ **Date** _____ **Score** _____

People / Animals

Directions: Write *A* if no change is needed. Write *B* or *C* if the given word should be capitalized.

_____ 1. Georges seurat was a famous French painter.

      A) correct   B) Seurat   C) Painter

_____ 2. A killer whale named Shamu is a star performer at Sea World.

      A) correct   B) Whale   C) Star

_____ 3. An ancient Greek writer of tragedies was sophocles.

      A) correct   B) Writer   C) Sophocles

_____ 4. In South Dakota is a memorial to the great Sioux chief, Crazy horse.

      A) correct   B) Chief   C) Horse

_____ 5. Alan b. Shepard was the first American in space.

      A) correct   B) B.   C) Space

Name _____ **Date** _____ **Score** _____

People / Animals

Directions: Write *A* if no change is needed. Write *B* or *C* if the given word should be capitalized.

_____ 1. Wednesday is my sister Nicole's birthday.

      A) correct   B) Sister   C) Birthday

_____ 2. Her best friend, judy, is having a party for her.

      A) correct   B) Judy   C) Her

_____ 3. Mona, Keri, and p.j. are making decorations.

      A) correct   B) P.J.   C) Decorations

_____ 4. My older brother steven is bringing Nicole.

      A) correct   B) Brother   C) Steven

_____ 5. Then mom, Dad, and I will yell "Surprise!"

      A) correct   B) Mom   C) Yell

Related materials for teaching Capitalization: Places / Locations
Reproducible: Pre-test and Post-test (page 36); Practice Page (page 35)
Enrichment Activity (page 34)
Rule Book Template (page 6); Individual Record Sheet (page 95)
"Practice With a Purpose": Places / Locations (pages 81-82)

Capitalization: Places / Locations

The ideas on these three pages follow the flow chart of suggested steps for teaching, reteaching, and testing presented on page 3 of this book.

STEP 1:
Motivation—Proper Geography

Begin by asking students to tell how each of these word pairs are alike and different: island–Iceland; sea–Mediterranean; mountain–Everest; country–Ireland; street–Flower Avenue. Students will note that the first word in each pair is a general geographic term, and the second is a specific example.

Present students with sentences containing a variety of geographical terms, both general and specific. Do not capitalize the names of the places. Ask students to copy and correct the sentences. Here is a suggested group with a number of different place references:

- I live on west maple road in carson, california.
- My home is just a few miles from the pacific ocean.
- On clear days you can see the offshore island of catalina from mt. wilson in nearby los angeles.
- Where I live, I can swim at hermosa beach one day and then drive northwest for less than two hours to ski near big bear lake the next!

STEP 2:
Pre-test and Grouping for Instruction

It is probable that some of your students do not capitalize proper place names. Following the exercise above, give all students the written pre-test (page 36). Record (or have students record) their scores on an individual record sheet (page 95). Sort through the record sheets and remove the tests of students who scored 100%. You may choose to give these students the post-test right away to verify mastery or wait to give it to them with the rest of the class. Form a group of students who scored 80% or lower for direct instruction and practice.

STEP 3:
Instruction

Present students with the same sentences used in the motivational activity. Underline each place name. Ask students if the place name is general or specific. Present the capitalization rule below and then go back over each place name asking students if it should be capitalized. (If you are using "Practice With a Purpose" coordinated mini-charts, use the rule page with this lesson.)

RULE 1 **Capitalize the names of specific places and locations.**

✓ **continents, countries, states, cities**   ✓ **islands, mountains**
✓ **oceans, lakes, rivers** ✓ **parks, forests, canyons** ✓ **street names**

NOTE! Capitalize direction words only when they refer to a section of the country or world or when they are part of a place name. Examples: the *east* side of town, but *East* Boston and *East* Third Street.

- I live on **West Maple Road** in **Carson**, **California**.
  West Maple Road, Carson, *and* California *are specific places.*

- My <u>home</u> is just a few miles from the **Pacific Ocean**.
  Home *is a general place;* Pacific Ocean *is a specific place.*

- On clear days you can see the offshore <u>island</u> of **Catalina** from **Mt. Wilson** in nearby **Los Angeles**.
  Island *is a general place;* Catalina, Mt. Wilson, *and* Los Angeles *are specific places.*

- Where I live, I can swim at **Hermosa Beach** one day and then drive northwest for less than two hours to ski near **Big Bear Lake** the next!
  Hermosa Beach *and* Big Bear Lake *are specific places. (Make certain students understand that* northwest *is not capitalized because it is not part of the name of a specific place.)*

STEP 4:
Apply and Practice

Following direct instruction, give students the opportunity to apply the skill in practice. You may use the prepared practice sheet provided (page 35), side two of the "Practice With a Purpose" mini-chart (page 82), or your own practice sentences. Students can use plain writing paper to copy and correct sentences you write on the board or those provided on the mini-chart. If you choose to use the reproducible practice sheet, duplicate only the number needed for your instructional group. (Wait for the pre-test results to determine the exact number of students who will need practice.)

Practice may be guided or done independently. Students may work individually, in pairs, or as a group. Correct the page together or privately to assess the need for reteaching before giving the post-test.

STEP 5:
Post-test and Reteaching

When your students have had sufficient instruction and practice, give the post-test. After recording scores on the individual record sheets, once again separate the sheets of those students who scored 80% or less on the post-test for reteaching. You may use or reuse any of the materials suggested in Step 4 for reteaching.

Follow-up / Enrichment

Once students have mastered the skill, make certain they retain it by giving a follow-up activity several weeks later. An excellent way to do this is to see if they can apply the skill in context. To check for retention, copy the postcard below onto chart paper. Have students rewrite it with correct capitalization. Or, if you prefer, use the prepared reproducible activity sheet on the following page. **Tip!** Let students make giant postcards. Have them copy the information given on one side and illustrate some aspect of Rome on the other.

To be corrected   *Corrections*

Dear John,
    Here we are in rome, italy! Today I walked on one of the oldest known roads, the appian way. We also went to a wonderful zoo in a big park called villa borghese. Tomorrow we will cross the tiber river to visit the observatory on mount mario; then we will go on to vatican city.
    Rome has to be one of the most fascinating places to visit in europe.

             Carmelle

TO:
John Zine
136 south fox lane
springfield, nj 07081

Rome, Italy
Appian Way
Villa Borghese
Tiber River
Mount Mario
Vatican City
Europe
South Fox Lane
Springfield
NJ

ANSWER KEYS

Pre-test:

1. B) Colorado
2. A) West
3. A) Rocky
4. A) Springs
5. B) United

Practice:

1. B) Harbor
2. B) City
3. B) United
4. B) France
5. A) Paris
6. A) Atlantic
7. B) Wood
8. B) Bedloe's
9. B) Liberty
10. A) Seine

Post-test:

1. B) Lane
2. B) New
3. A) Georgia
4. A) America
5. B) Pacific

Practice With a Purpose—
Places / Locations

1. Asia; Japan
2. Ginza Avenue; Tokyo
3. Japan; Honshu
4. Honshu; Inland Sea
5. Mt. Fuji

Places / Locations

Use the rules you have learned for capitalizing names of specific places to find and circle errors on this postcard. Then rewrite the message and address correctly on the lines.

Dear John,

Here we are in rome, italy! Today I walked on one of the oldest known roads, the appian way. We also went to a wonderful zoo in a big park called villa borghese. Tomorrow we will cross the tiber river to visit the observatory on mount mario; then we will go on to vatican city.

Rome has to be one of the most fascinating places to visit in europe.

Carmelle

ITALY

TO:
John Zine
136 south fox lane
springfield, nj 07081

_____
_____
_____
_____
_____
_____
_____
_____
_____
_____
_____
_____

Places / Locations

Directions: Read carefully. Choose the answer that shows the correct capitalization. Circle *A* or *B*.

A Great American Lady

1. Have you ever been to New York harbor?

2. No one who has could miss the 151-foot-tall lady who greets visitors to New York city.

3. She is, of course, the Statue of Liberty— a symbol of freedom in the united States.

4. The statue was a gift from france in 1884.

5. It was designed and built in paris by Frédéric Auguste Bartholdi.

6. It was shipped across the atlantic Ocean in 214 cases aboard the French ship *Isère*.

7. The site chosen for the statue was the center of an old fort named Fort wood.

8. Fort Wood was located on bedloe's Island in New York Harbor.

9. Later, the island's name was changed to liberty Island.

10. A small model of the statue still stands above the seine River in Paris.

Statue of Liberty

1. A) new	B) Harbor	6. A) Atlantic	B) Ship
2. A) Lady	B) City	7. A) Site	B) Wood
3. A) Freedom	B) United	8. A) wood	B) Bedloe's
4. A) Gift	B) France	9. A) Island's	B) Liberty
5. A) Paris	B) bartholdi	10. A) Seine	B) River

Places / Locations

Directions: Read carefully. Choose the answer that shows which word should be capitalized. Circle *A* or *B*.

1. My uncle lives in a town in colorado.

2. His house is on west Pike Road, a street named after Zebulon Pike.

3. Over 150 years ago, Zebulon Pike attempted to climb the rocky Mountains' famous Pikes Peak.

4. Today, Colorado springs lies only six miles to the east.

5. Right from his front door, my uncle enjoys one of the most beautiful views in the united States.

1. A) Town	B) Colorado
2. A) West	B) Street
3. A) Rocky	B) Famous
4. A) Springs	B) East
5. A) Views	B) United

Places / Locations

Directions: Read carefully. Choose the answer that shows the correct capitalization. Circle *A* or *B*.

1. My street, Whitney lane, is named after the inventor of the cotton gin, Eli Whitney.

2. Eli was born in Westboro, Massachusetts, but lived here in new Haven, Connecticut.

3. While visiting a cotton plantation in georgia, he got an idea for a machine that could separate the seeds from cotton.

4. Unfortunately, at that time america did not have patent laws.

5. Eli's idea was copied throughout the United States and even across the pacific Ocean.

1. A) street	B) Lane
2. A) haven	B) New
3. A) Georgia	B) Idea
4. A) America	B) Patent
5. A) united	B) Pacific

Related materials for teaching Capitalization: Special Things
Reproducible: Pre-test and Post-test (page 42); Practice Page (page 41)
Enrichment Activity (page 40)
Rule Book Template (page 6); Individual Record Sheet (page 95)
"Practice With a Purpose": Special Things (pages 83-84)

Capitalization: Special Things

The ideas on these three pages follow the flow chart of suggested steps
for teaching, reteaching, and testing presented on page 3 of this book.

STEP 1:
Motivation—Notable Nouns

Introduce the skill by dividing the class into small groups. Give each group a sheet of chart
paper. Instruct each group to work together to make a list that names one or more specific examples of each of the following general things:

- names of ships
- names of aircraft
- names of spacecraft
- names of paintings
- names of sculptures

- names of planets
- names of stars or constellations
- names of buildings
- names of monuments
- names of landmarks

Let each group post its list and read it to the class. Note students' use (or nonuse) of capitalization on their lists, but do not comment at this time. Below is an example of how an uncor-
rected group chart may look:

ships: *titanic, Mayflower*
aircraft: *Air force I*, stealth fighter
spacecraft: *challenger*
painting: *mona lisa*
sculpture: statue of liberty
planets: mercury, Venus, Pluto
constellation: gemini
buildings: Taj Mahal, white house
monuments: Washington monument,
memorials to veterans
landmarks: Rock of Gibraltar

STEP 2:
Pre-test and Grouping for Instruction

Follow the motivational activity by giving all students the written pre-test (page 42). Record (or have students record) their scores on an individual record sheet (page 95). Sort through the record sheets and remove the tests of students who scored 100%. You may choose to give these students the post-test right away to verify mastery or wait to give it to them with the rest of the class. Form a group of students who scored 80% or lower for direct instruction and practice.

STEP 3:
Instruction

Present the rule given to students. Then discuss each group chart. First determine the validity of each item included on the list. Draw a line through any invalid item and explain why it is invalid. Then ask each student to recopy the group's chart correctly capitalized. (If you are using the "Practice With a Purpose" coordinated mini-charts, use the rule page with this lesson.)

RULE 1
👉 **Capitalize the names of specific ships, aircraft and spacecraft, works of art, celestial bodies, buildings, monuments, and landmarks.**

ships: *Titanic, Mayflower*
aircraft: *Air Force I*, ~~stealth fighter~~ *(Stealth fighter is not a specific name.)*
spacecraft: *Challenger*
painting: *Mona Lisa*
sculpture: Statue of Liberty
planets: Mercury, Venus, Pluto
constellation: Gemini
buildings: Taj Mahal, White House
monuments: Washington Monument, ~~memorials to veterans~~ *(Memorials to veterans is not specific.)*
landmarks: Rock of Gibraltar

STEP 4:
Apply and Practice

Following direct instruction, give students the opportunity to apply the skill in practice. You may use the prepared practice sheet provided (page 41), side two of the "Practice With a Purpose" mini-chart (page 84), or your own practice sentences. Students can use plain writing paper to copy and correct sentences you write on the board or those provided on the mini-chart. If you choose to use the reproducible practice sheet, duplicate only the number needed for your instructional group. (Wait for the pre-test results to determine the exact number of students who will need practice.)

Practice may be guided or done independently. Students may work individually, in pairs, or as a group. Correct the page together or privately to assess the need for reteaching before giving the post-test.

STEP 5:
Post-test and Reteaching

When your students have had sufficient instruction and practice, give the post-test. After recording scores on the individual record sheets, once again separate the sheets of those students who scored 80% or less on the post-test for reteaching. You may use or reuse any of the materials suggested in Step 4 for reteaching.

Follow-up / Enrichment

Once students have mastered the skill, make certain they retain it by giving a follow-up activity several weeks later. An excellent way to do this is to see if they can apply the skill in context. To check for retention, copy the sentences below onto chart paper. Have students categorize the underlined terms as general or specific and then write the sentences capitalized correctly. Or, if you prefer, use the prepared reproducible activity sheet on the following page. **Tip!** Challenge students to write more facts naming specific ships, works of art, celestial bodies, buildings, and monuments.

To be corrected

1. The <u>kremlin</u> is a famous group of <u>buildings</u> in Moscow.
2. The <u>louvre</u> is an art <u>museum</u> in Paris.
5. The document ending World War II was signed aboard the <u>battleship</u> USS *missouri*.
3. The <u>big dipper</u> is part of a larger <u>constellation</u> called <u>ursa major</u>.
4. Da Vinci's <u>painting</u> of a smiling woman is called the *mona lisa*.

Corrected

General Names
buildings, museum, battleship, constellation, painting

Specific Names
Kremlin, Louvre, *Missouri*, Big Dipper, Ursa Major, *Mona Lisa*

1. The <u>Kremlin</u> is a famous group of <u>buildings</u> in Moscow.
2. The <u>Louvre</u> is an art <u>museum</u> in Paris.
3. The document ending World War II was signed aboard the <u>battleship</u> USS *Missouri*.
4. The <u>Big Dipper</u> is part of a larger <u>constellation</u> called <u>Ursa Major</u>.
5. Da Vinci's <u>painting</u> of a smiling woman is called the *Mona Lisa*.

ANSWER KEYS

Pre-test:
1. A) Great Wall of China
2. B) Mount Rushmore
3. B) Pyramids of Giza
4. A) Venus and Earth
5. B) USS *Constitution*

Practice:
1. B) *Mayflower*
2. C) both
3. B) Big
4. A) *Blue*
5. C) both
6. A) Palace
7. D) neither
8. C) both
9. D) neither
10. B) Louvre

Post-test:
1. A) *The Three Musicians*
2. B) Empire State Building
3. B) *Spirit of St. Louis*
4. B) Sydney Opera House
5. B) Milky Way

Practice With a Purpose— Special Things
1. Saturn
2. *The Starry Night*
3. Parthenon
4. *Nautilus*
5. Lincoln Memorial

Special Things

Read the facts. List each underlined term beside the category to which it belongs. Then rewrite the sentences correctly on the lines below.

Fascinating Facts

1. The <u>kremlin</u> is a famous group of <u>buildings</u> in Moscow.

2. The <u>louvre</u> is an art <u>museum</u> in Paris.

3. The document ending World War II was signed aboard the <u>battleship</u> USS <u>*missouri*</u>.

4. The <u>big dipper</u> is part of a larger <u>constellation</u> called <u>ursa major</u>.

5. Da Vinci's <u>painting</u> of a smiling woman is called the <u>*mona lisa*</u>.

Ursa Major (Great Bear)

General Names: _____

_____

Specific Names: _____

_____

_____

Fascinating Facts

_____

_____

_____

_____

_____

_____

_____

_____

_____

_____

Special Things

Directions: Circle the letter of the choice that shows which word or words, if any, should be capitalized in each statement.

1. The Pilgrims came to America aboard the *mayflower*.
   A) Aboard   B) *Mayflower*   C) both   D) neither

2. A well-known Australian tourist attraction is ayers rock.
   A) Ayers   B) Rock   C) both   D) neither

3. The most famous clock in the world is big Ben.
   A) Clock   B) Big   C) both   D) neither

4. *The blue Boy* is a portrait by Gainsborough.
   A) *Blue*   B) Portrait   C) both   D)neither

5. The satellite *mariner 9* orbits mars.
   A) *Mariner*   B) Mars   C) both   D) neither

6. London's Buckingham palace is the home of English royalty.
   A) Palace   B) Royalty   C) both   D) neither

7. Two famous Civil War battleships are the *Monitor* and the *Merrimack*.
   A) Famous   B) Battleships   C) both   D) neither

8. The golden gate Bridge stretches across San Francisco Bay.
   A) Golden   B) Gate   C) both   D) neither

9. The U.S. Capitol houses the legislative branch of the U.S. government.
   A) Legislative   B) Government   C) both   D) neither

10. The painting *Whistler's Mother* hangs in the louvre in Paris.
    A) Painting   B) Louvre   C) both   D) neither

Special Things

Directions: Circle the letter of the choice that shows correct capitalization of the answer to each description.

1. a 1500-mile long landmark:
   A) Great Wall of China   B) great wall of China

2. a sculptured memorial to four U.S. presidents:
   A) mount rushmore   B) Mount Rushmore

3. Egyptian tributes to dead pharaohs:
   A) pyramids of giza   B) Pyramids of Giza

4. known as the twin planets:
   A) Venus and Earth   B) venus and earth

5. ship whose nickname is "Old Ironsides":
   A) USS *constitution*   B) USS *Constitution*

Special Things

Directions: Circle the letter of the choice that shows correct capitalization of the answer to each description.

1. Pablo Picasso's painting: A) *The Three Musicians*   B) *the three Musicans*

2. tallest building in New York: A) empire State building   B) Empire State Building

3. Charles Lindbergh's plane: A) *spirit of St. Louis*   B) *Spirit of St. Louis*

4. Australian landmark: A) Sydney opera house   B) Sydney Opera House

5. name of our galaxy: A) milky way   B) Milky Way

Related materials for teaching Capitalization: Groups / Languages
Reproducible: Pre-test and Post-test (page 48); Practice Page (page 47)
Enrichment Activity (page 46)
Rule Book Template (page 6); Individual Record Sheet (page 95)
"Practice With a Purpose": Groups / Languages (pages 85-86)

Capitalization: Groups / Languages

The ideas on these three pages follow the flow chart of suggested steps for teaching, reteaching, and testing presented on page 3 of this book.

STEP 1:
Motivation—Organized People

This lesson covers capitalization of references to various groups of people—nations, nationalities, cultures, religions, religious groups, agencies, organizations, clubs, companies, businesses, and schools. It also covers capitalization of references to languages.

Introduce the lesson by presenting the sentences below. Ask students to copy the sentences. Tell them to capitalize terms as needed.

- The olympic committee selects sites for the Olympic Games.
- Both french and english are main languages in canada.
- The Koran is the sacred book of muslims.
- The tucson electric power company provides electricity to residents in Tucson, Arizona.
- The united nations is a world-wide peace-keeping organization.
- Not much is known about why the mayan culture disappeared.
- Afternoon tea is a well-known british custom.

STEP 2:
Pre-test and Grouping for Instruction

The sentences in the motivational activity cover a variety of proper nouns referring to groups of people. Follow this introduction by giving all students the written pre-test (page 48). Record (or have students record) their scores on an individual record sheet (page 95). Sort through the record sheets and remove the tests of students who scored 100%. You may choose to give these students the post-test right away to verify mastery or wait to give it to them with the rest of the class. Form a group of students who scored 80% or lower for direct instruction and practice.

STEP 3:
Instruction

Correct the sentences used in the motivational activity. Have students underline the corrected capitalized terms. Ask them to speculate about why each term should be capitalized. Then present the two rules that follow. (If you are using the "Practice With a Purpose" coordinated mini-charts, use the rule page with this lesson.)

- The <u>Olympic Committee</u> selects sites for the Olympic Games.
- Both <u>French</u> and <u>English</u> are main languages in <u>Canada</u>.
- The Koran is the sacred book of <u>Muslims</u>.
- The <u>Tucson Electric Power Company</u> provides electricity to residents in Tucson, Arizona.
- The <u>United Nations</u> is a world-wide peace-keeping organization.
- Not much is known about why the <u>Mayan</u> culture disappeared.
- Afternoon tea is a well-known <u>British</u> custom.

RULE 1   **Capitalize names of specific groups.**

  ✓ **nations, nationalities, cultures** *(Canada, Mayan, British)*
  ✓ **religions, religious groups** *(Muslims)*
  ✓ **agencies, organizations, clubs** *(Olympic Committee, United Nations)*
  ✓ **companies, businesses, schools** *(Tucson Electric Power Company)*

RULE 2   **Capitalize names of languages.** *(French, English)*

STEP 4:
Apply and Practice

Following direct instruction, give students the opportunity to apply the skill in practice. You may use the prepared practice sheet provided (page 47), side two of the "Practice With a Purpose" mini-chart (page 86), or your own practice sentences. Students can use plain writing paper to copy and correct sentences you write on the board or those provided on the mini-chart. If you choose to use the reproducible practice sheet, duplicate only the number needed for your instructional group. (Wait for the pre-test results to determine the exact number of students who will need practice.)

Practice may be guided or done independently. Students may work individually, in pairs, or as a group. Correct the page together or privately to assess the need for reteaching before giving the post-test.

STEP 5:
Post-test and Reteaching

When your students have had sufficient instruction and practice, give the post-test. After recording scores on the individual record sheets, once again separate the sheets of those students who scored 80% or less on the post-test for reteaching. You may use or reuse any of the materials suggested in Step 4 for reteaching.

Follow-up / Enrichment

Once students have mastered the skill, make certain they retain it by giving a follow-up activity several weeks later. An excellent way to do this is to see if they can apply the skill in context. Copy the activity at the right onto chart paper to check for retention. Ask students to follow the directions given. Or, if you prefer, use the prepared reproducible activity sheet on the following page. **Tip!** Let students create word search puzzles based on their answers.

To be completed

Directions: Copy and complete each description with a specific example. Capitalize as needed.

1. a nationality of South America:
2. a Christian religion:
3. an airline company:
4. a business in your community:
5. a government agency:
6. an ancient culture:
7. a specific school:
8. a national organization:
9. a language spoken in Europe:
10. a specific club:

Completed

Students' answers will vary, but should be appropriately capitalized as shown in the following sample:

1. a nationality of South America: **B**razilian
2. a Christian religion: **L**utheran
3. an airline company: **U**nited **A**ir Lines
4. a business in your community: **H**ughes **C**orp.
5. a government agency: **T**reasury **D**epartment
6. an ancient culture: **E**gyptian
7. a specific school: **U**niversity of **M**aryland
8. a national organization: **L**eague of **W**omen **V**oters
9. a language spoken in Europe: **G**erman
10. a specific club: **C**hess **C**lub

ANSWER KEYS

Pre-test:

1. B) Buddhists
2. A) Naval Academy
3. B) Canadian
4. A) Chrysler Corp.
5. B) Thai

Practice:

1. A) Junior Service League
2. B) Carver High School
3. B) American
4. A) Chinese
5. B) China
6. B) religions
7. A) United States
8. B) Multicultural Club
9. B) English
10. B) Su Lin's Bakery

Post-test:

1. B) Catholic
2. A) Ford Motor Co.
3. A) Native-American
4. B) Senate
5. A) French

**Practice With a Purpose—
Groups / Languages**

1. Census Bureau
2. Dutch
3. National Football League
4. Harvard
5. Aborigines

Groups / Languages

Use the rules you have learned for capitalizing the names of groups and languages to complete each description with a specific example.

1. a nationality of South America: _____

2. a Christian religion: _____

3. an airline company: _____

4. a business in your community: _____

5. a government agency: _____

6. an ancient culture: _____

7. a specific school: _____

8. a national organization: _____

9. a language spoken in Europe: _____

10. a specific club: _____

Use your answers to make a word search puzzle below. Trade with a friend to solve.

Groups / Languages

Directions: Write the letter of the choice that shows the correct capitalization of the missing word or words.

Cultural Exchange

The __(1)__ of __(2)__ is sponsoring a dinner to promote cultural exchange between __(3)__ and __(4)__ students. The American students will have a chance to learn about the customs and lifestyles in __(5)__, including a look at some ancient and traditional __(6)__ widely practiced there. Chinese students will have the opportunity to explore the cultural diversity found in the __(7)__. All students will be treated to a presentation by the __(8)__, which has prepared a selection of folk songs in both __(9)__ and Chinese. Refreshments will be served compliments of __(10)__.

_____ 1. A) Junior Service League   B) junior Service League

_____ 2. A) Carver high school   B) Carver High School

_____ 3. A) american   B) American

_____ 4. A) Chinese   B) chinese

_____ 5. A) china   B) China

_____ 6. A) Religions   B) religions

_____ 7. A) United States   B) united states

_____ 8. A) Multicultural club   B) Multicultural Club

_____ 9. A) english   B) English

_____ 10. A) Su Lin's bakery   B) Su Lin's Bakery

Name _____ **Date** _____ **Score** _____

Groups / Languages

Directions: Circle the letter of the choice that shows the correct capitalization of the answer that completes each sentence.

1. Followers of the teachings of Buddha are called ___.
   A) buddhists   B) Buddhists

2. The U.S. ___ is in Annapolis, Maryland.
   A) Naval Academy   B) naval Academy

3. A red maple leaf appears on the ___ flag.
   A) canadian   B) Canadian

4. ___ is a company that makes cars.
   A) Chrysler Corp.   B) Chrysler corp.

5. The people of Thailand speak ___.
   A) thai   B) Thai

Flag of Canada

Name _____ **Date** _____ **Score** _____

Groups / Languages

Directions: Circle the letter of the choice that shows the correct capitalization of the answer that completes each sentence.

Hopi Shelter

1. The Pope is the living leader of the ___ religion.
   A) catholic   B) Catholic

2. The founder of the ___ was Henry Ford.
   A) Ford Motor Co.   B) Ford motor co.

3. The Hopi and Navajo are ___ cultures.
   A) Native-American   B) native-American

4. Representatives in the ___ are called senators.
   A) senate   B) Senate

5. The words *bon appetit* are ___ for "good appetite."
   A) French   B) french

Capitalization: Events / Documents

The ideas on these three pages follow the flow chart of suggested steps
for teaching, reteaching, and testing presented on page 3 of this book.

STEP 1:

Motivation—Historical Perspective

Although the capitalization rules in this lesson apply to all specific events and documents, the
exercises focus on history. Introduce the skill by presenting students with the following paragraph
about the Civil War. Ask students to copy the paragraph, underline references to specific events
and documents, and capitalize as needed.

In 1850 Congress passed the fugitive
slave law, which gave slave owners the
right to pursue and recapture their
"property." Northern states responded
by passing the personal liberty acts,
which guaranteed protection and a fair
trial to recaptured slaves. Lincoln's
emancipation proclamation in 1863
declared slaves to be free. The civil war,
as much about economics as human
rights, became a bloody battle of
American versus American. The era that
followed, known as reconstruction, was
a painful period of transition, the effects
of which are still being felt.

STEP 2:

Pre-test and Grouping for Instruction

Following this introduction, give all students the written pre-test (page 54). Record (or have
students record) their scores on an individual record sheet (page 95). Sort through the record
sheets and remove the tests of students who scored 100%. You may choose to give these students the post-test right away to verify mastery or wait to give it to them with the rest of the class.
Form a group of students who scored 80% or lower for direct instruction and practice.

STEP 3:
Instruction

Introduce the capitalization of events and documents by reviewing the paragraph given in the motivational activity. Point out the nature of each underlined item. Present the capitalization rules given and then have students correct their own paragraphs. (If you are using the "Practice With a Purpose" coordinated mini-charts, use the rule page with this lesson.)

RULE 1 ☞ **Capitalize names of specific events and time periods.**

✓ Fugitive Slave Law
✓ Personal Liberty Acts
✓ Civil War
✓ Reconstruction

RULE 2 ☞ **Capitalize names of specific documents, declarations, and acts.**

✓ Emancipation Proclamation

In 1850 Congress passed the <u>Fugitive Slave Law</u>, which gave slave owners the right to pursue and recapture their "property." Northern states responded by passing the <u>Personal Liberty Acts</u>, which guaranteed protection and a fair trial to recaptured slaves. Lincoln's <u>Emancipation Proclamation</u> in 1863 declared slaves to be free. The <u>Civil War</u>, as much about economics as human rights, became a bloody battle of American versus American. The era that followed, known as <u>Reconstruction</u>, was a painful period of transition, the effects of which are still being felt.

STEP 4:
Apply and Practice

Following direct instruction, give students the opportunity to apply the skill in practice. You may use the prepared practice sheet provided (page 53), side two of the "Practice With a Purpose" mini-chart (page 88), or your own practice sentences. Students can use plain writing paper to copy and correct sentences you write on the board or those provided on the mini-chart. If you choose to use the reproducible practice sheet, duplicate only the number needed for your instructional group. (Wait for the pre-test results to determine the exact number of students who will need practice.)

Practice may be guided or done independently. Students may work individually, in pairs, or as a group. Correct the page together or privately to assess the need for reteaching before giving the post-test.

STEP 5:
Post-test and Reteaching

When your students have had sufficient instruction and practice, give the post-test. After recording scores on the individual record sheets, once again separate the sheets of those students who scored 80% or less on the post-test for reteaching. You may use or reuse any of the materials suggested in Step 4 for reteaching.

Follow-up / Enrichment

Once students have mastered the skill, make certain they retain it by giving a follow-up activity several weeks later. Below are six events that took place between the years 1870 and 1920. Copy the sentences onto chart paper. To check for retention, have students write the events in chronological order, with correct capitalization. Or, if you prefer, use the prepared reproducible activity sheet on the following page. **Tip!** Challenge students to research and write about six historic events from another 50-year time span.

To be corrected

- The selective service act of 1917 set up a mandatory military draft in the United States.
- In 1919 the Eighteenth Amendment to the U.S. constitution passed, beginning a period known as prohibition.
- Victory in the russo-japanese war of 1904 earned Japan respect as an emerging world power.
- The 1914 assassination of Archduke Ferdinand of Austria triggered the start of world war I.
- After the defeat of France in the franco-prussian war of 1870, Germany reunited and formed the Second Reich.
- Following the loss of many lives in the russian revolution, Communist forces gained control in 1920.

Corrections (abbreviated)

Correct sentence order and capitalization:

(1) After . . . <u>Franco-Prussian War</u> . . .

(2) Victory . . . <u>Russo-Japanese War</u> . . .

(3) The 1914 . . . <u>World War</u> . . .

(4) The <u>Selective Service Act</u> . . .

(5) In 1919 . . . <u>Constitution</u> . . . <u>Prohibition</u>

(6) Following . . . <u>Russian Revolution</u> . . .

ANSWER KEYS

Pre-test:
1. B) Renaissance
2. A) Bill of Rights
3. B) Great Depression
4. A) Civil War
5. B) Stamp Act

Practice:
1. B) Great Depression
2. A) Treaty of Versailles
3. A) World War I
4. B) Neutrality Acts
5. A) Lend-Lease Act
6. B) Operation Barbarossa
7. B) World War II
8. B) Pearl Harbor Day
9. A) V-E Day
10. A) Atomic Age

Post-test:
1. B) Emancipation Proclamation
2. A) Stone Age
3. B) Louisiana Purchase
4. A) Desert Storm
5. B) Agricultural Revolution

Practice With a Purpose— Events / Documents

(1) Europe's Dark Ages . . . *(2)* In 1215 . . . Magna Carta.
(3) In 1815 . . . French Revolution . . . Battle of Waterloo.
(4) American . . . Boston Tea Party . . . *(5)* The Roaring Twenties . . .

Events / Documents

Below are six events that took place in the 50 years between 1870 and 1920. Write the events in chronological order. Use the rules you have learned about capitalizing events and documents to capitalize each statement correctly.

- The selective service act of 1917 set up a mandatory military draft in the United States.

- In 1919 the Eighteenth Amendment to the U.S. constitution passed, beginning a period known as prohibition.

- Victory in the russo-japanese war of 1904 earned Japan respect as an emerging world power.

- The 1914 assassination of Archduke Ferdinand of Austria triggered the start of world war I.

- After the defeat of France in the franco-prussian war of 1870, Germany reunited and formed the Second Reich.

- Following the loss of many lives in the russian revolution, Communist forces gained control in 1920.

Fifty Years of World Events

_____

_____

_____

_____

_____

_____

_____

_____

_____

_____

_____

_____

_____

_____

_____

_____

_____

_____

Events / Documents

Directions: Write the letter of the choice that shows the correct capitalization of the missing word or words.

World War II

In 1930 the __(1)__ had taken hold of the industrialized nations of the world. The German people were especially hard hit and suffering from poverty and unemployment. In violation of the __(2)__, Adolf Hitler began rebuilding Germany and promised to restore it to its former strength. Weary from __(3)__, Britain and France were reluctant to resist. America's __(4)__ kept her from getting involved, but the __(5)__ allowed the United States to lend war supplies to threatened nations. The Soviets believed they were safe until Hitler launched __(6)__, a surprise attack on them.

On December 7, 1941, Japan attacked the United States at Pearl Harbor and America entered __(7)__.

More than four years after __(8)__, the Allies claimed victory in Europe—__(9)__— on May 8, 1945. The war in the Pacific ended with the dropping of the atomic bomb on Japan. World War II was over, but the __(10)__ brought new, more fearsome threats of war and destruction for the future.

_____ 1. A) great depression   B) Great Depression

_____ 2. A) Treaty of Versailles   B) treaty of Versailles

_____ 3. A) World War I   B) World war I

_____ 4. A) Neutrality acts   B) Neutrality Acts

_____ 5. A) Lend-Lease Act   B) Lend-Lease act

_____ 6. A) operation Barbarossa   B) Operation Barbarossa

_____ 7. A) world war II   B) World War II

_____ 8. A) pearl harbor day   B) Pearl Harbor Day

_____ 9. A) V-E Day   B) V-E day

_____ 10. A) Atomic Age   B) atomic age

Events / Documents

Directions: Circle the letter of the choice that shows the correct capitalization of the answer to the description.

1. Europe's period of "rebirth":
   A) renaissance   B) Renaissance

2. document guaranteeing American freedoms:
   A) Bill of Rights   B) Bill of rights

3. a period of economic hardship in the 1930s:
   A) great Depression   B) Great Depression

4. the war between the North and South:
   A) Civil War   B) Civil war

5. British tax on American colonists:
   A) Stamp act   B) Stamp Act

Events / Documents

Directions: Circle the letter of the choice that shows the correct capitalization of the answer to the description.

1. Lincoln's declaration that slaves be free:
   A) Emancipation proclamation   B) Emancipation Proclamation

2. period when stones were used for tools and weapons:
   A) Stone Age   B) stone Age

3. agreement by which the United States acquired the Louisiana Territory:
   A) Louisiana purchase   B) Louisiana Purchase

4. the 1991 war to free Kuwait:
   A) Desert Storm   B) desert storm

5. the change over from hunting to farming:
   A) agricultural revolution   B) Agricultural Revolution

Related materials for teaching Capitalization: Titles of Respect
Reproducible: Pre-test and Post-test (page 60); Practice Page (page 59)
Enrichment Activity (page 58)
Rule Book Template (page 6); Individual Record Sheet (page 95)
"Practice With a Purpose": Titles of Respect (pages 89-90)

Capitalization: Titles of Respect

The ideas on these three pages follow the flow chart of suggested steps for teaching, reteaching, and testing presented on page 3 of this book.

STEP 1:
Motivation—Respectfully Speaking

Introduce the skill by presenting sentences containing a mix of general and specific titles. Ask students to rewrite the sentences capitalized correctly. Here are some suggested sentences:

- Several **doctors** attended the meeting. The first speaker was **dr.** Emanuel.
- George Washington was a **general** in the Revolutionary War. Later he was asked to be the first **president** of the United States. **general** Washington became **president** Washington.
- The **senator** addressed the **judge**. "What is your opinion, **your honor**?" he asked.
- My **aunt** just graduated from medical school. Now I proudly call her **aunt** Sara, **m.d.**
- As soon as my **grandfather** sat in the chair, my little brother jumped into his lap. They both smiled as **grandpa** gave him a big hug.
- My neighbors, **mr.** and **mrs.** Olsen, have a new baby. They named him Michael Olsen, **Jr.**

STEP 2:
Pre-test and Grouping for Instruction

Check students' skill at recognizing correct capitalization in titles of respect by giving all students the written pre-test (page 60). Record (or have students record) their scores on an individual record sheet (page 95). Sort through the record sheets and remove the tests of students who scored 100%. You may choose to give these students the post-test right away to verify mastery or wait to give it to them with the rest of the class. Form a group of students who scored 80% or lower for direct instruction and practice.

Mr. and Mrs. Olsen
with Michael Olsen, Jr.

STEP 3:
Instruction

Present the capitalization rule below. Then use the sentences from the motivational activity as examples. Discuss the boldfaced words in each sentence. Ask students to tell if the word should be capitalized and why. The corrected terms are given below, classified by reason. (If you are using the "Practice With a Purpose" coordinated mini-charts, use the rule page with this lesson.)

RULE 1 ☛ **Capitalize the title of a person when it is part of, or takes the place of, the person's name.**

✓ The **captain** took the helm. *(not part of a name)*
✓ "What is our heading?" asked **Captain** Davidson. *(part of a name)*
✓ "We are sailing due west, **Captain**," answered the first mate. *(replaces a name)*
NOTE! Capitalize abbreviations of titles, too. ✓ **Capt.** Davidson *(abbreviation)*

Not Capitalized— *Not part of a specific person's name:*	Capitalized— *Part of a specific person's name:*	Capitalized— *Takes the place of a specific person's name:*
. . . **doctors** attended . . .	. . . **Dr.** Emanuel.	
. . . a **general** . . .	. . . **General** Washington.	. . . **Your Honor**?
. . . the first **president** of . . .	. . . **President** Washington . . .	. . . **Grandpa** . . .
The **senator** . . .	. . . **Aunt** Sara, **M.D.**	
. . . the **judge**.	. . . **Mr.** and **Mrs.** Olsen . . .	
My **aunt** . . .	. . . Michael Olsen, **Jr.**	
. . . my **grandfather** . . .		

STEP 4:
Apply and Practice

Following direct instruction, give students the opportunity to apply the skill in practice. You may use the prepared practice sheet provided (page 59), side two of the "Practice With a Purpose" mini-chart (page 90), or your own practice sentences. Students can use plain writing paper to copy and correct sentences you write on the board or those provided on the mini-chart. If you choose to use the reproducible practice sheet, duplicate only the number needed for your instructional group. (Wait for the pre-test results to determine the exact number of students who will need practice.)

Practice may be guided or done independently. Students may work individually, in pairs, or as a group. Correct the page together or privately to assess the need for reteaching before giving the post-test.

STEP 5:
Post-test and Reteaching

When your students have had sufficient instruction and practice, give the post-test. After recording scores on the individual record sheets, once again separate the sheets of those students who scored 80% or less on the post-test for reteaching. You may use or reuse any of the materials suggested in Step 4 for reteaching.

Follow-up / Enrichment

Once students have mastered the skill, make certain they retain it by giving a follow-up activity several weeks later. An excellent way to do this is to see if they can apply the skill in context. At the right is an exercise you can copy onto chart paper to check for retention. Ask students to imagine holding each of the positions given. Then direct them to write how their nameplate would read, complete with their title. For example, as mayor, student Sonya Bradford's nameplate would read Mayor Bradford. **Tip!** Let students draw how they envision themselves at work 20 years in the future. Or, if you prefer, use the prepared reproducible activity sheet on the following page.

To be completed

What's in a Name?
Directions: Write your name, including your title, if you were
- president of the United States
- police chief of your city
- a medical doctor
- state governor
- a United States senator
- a military captain
- a justice of the Supreme Court
- a university professor
- an ambassador
- principal of your school

Completed

Students' answers will vary, but should include the appropriate title, capitalized as shown in the following sample:
President Bradford
Chief Bradford
Dr. Bradford or Sonya Bradford, **M.D.**
Governor Bradford
Senator Bradford
Captain Bradford
Justice Bradford
Professor Bradford
Ambassador Bradford
Principal Bradford

ANSWER KEYS

Pre-test:
1. A) correct
2. B) Mr.
3. A) correct
4. B) Governor
5. B) Jr.

Practice:
1. B) Professor
2. A) correct
3. A) correct
4. B) President
5. B) Aunt
6. A) correct
7. A) correct
8. B) Governor
9. A) correct
10. B) Mom

Post-test:
1. B) Dad
2. B) President
3. B) D.D.S.
4. A) correct
5. B) Mrs.

Practice With a Purpose—Titles of Respect
1. Dr. / Mrs.   2. Jr.   3. correct   4. correct   5. Officer

Titles of Respect

What would you like to be someday? Imagine yourself in each of the respected positions listed below. Use the rules you have learned for capitalizing titles to write how your nameplate would read, complete with your title.

Example: If Sonya Bradford grew up to be mayor, she would be called Mayor Bradford.

• president of the United States _____

• police chief of your city _____

• a medical doctor _____

• state governor _____

• a United States senator _____

• a military captain _____

• a justice of the Supreme Court _____

• a university professor _____

• an ambassador _____

• principal of your school _____

BONUS!

Look into the future. What kind of work do you see yourself doing? In the crystal ball, draw yourself at work 20 years from now.
On the lines below, write your job title and describe what you do.

_____

_____

_____

_____

_____

_____

_____

Titles of Respect

Directions: Write *A* in the blanks at the bottom of the page if the numbered word is correct as is. Write *B* if it should be capitalized.

The head of the archeological dig, professor Mary Gibbs, confirmed the findings.
                                                   (1)

"This is definitely the bone of a Rex!" exclaimed the professor.
                                                     (2)

Four living presidents attended the memorial service for president Nixon.
                    (3)   (4)

Yesterday aunt Susan came for dinner. She brought a gift for her sister, my mom.
    (5)   (6)

The governor asked for a vote on the matter. Three of the five committee
       (7)

members voted for governor McDean's proposal.
                   (8)

The girls approached their mother. "May we keep the kitten, mom?" they asked.
                            (9)   (10)

---

(1) _____   (3) _____   (5) _____   (7) _____   (9) _____

(2) _____   (4) _____   (6) _____   (8) _____   (10) _____

Name _____ Date _____ Score _____

Titles of Respect

Directions: Write *A* if the numbered word is correct as is. Write *B* if it should be capitalized.

_____ The doctor looked at the x-ray.
(1)

_____ "The play was excellent," said mr. Han.
(2)

_____ The captain landed the plane smoothly.
(3)

_____ I am going to write to governor Atkins about this problem.
(4)

_____ Joseph Brown, jr., is running for mayor.
(5)

Name _____ Date _____ Score _____

Titles of Respect

Directions: Write *A* if the numbered word is correct as is. Write *B* if it should be capitalized.

_____ "Let's go to the game Saturday, dad," I said.
(1)

_____ The reporter asked, "Is that your policy, Mr. president?"
(2)

_____ "I went to the office marked G. Glenn, d.d.s.
(3)

_____ The general gave the order and the troops moved out.
(4)

_____ Mr. and mrs. Kaplan donated money to the project.
(5)

Related materials for teaching Capitalization: Titles of Works
Reproducible: Pre-test and Post-test (page 66); Practice Page (page 65)
Enrichment Activity (page 64)
Rule Book Template (page 6); Individual Record Sheet (page 95)
"Practice With a Purpose": Titles of Works (pages 91-92)

Capitalization: Titles of Works

The ideas on these three pages follow the flow chart of suggested steps for teaching, reteaching, and testing presented on page 3 of this book.

STEP 1:
Motivation—Not All Equal

This lesson covers general guidelines for the capitalization of titles—books, chapters, stories, articles, newspapers, magazines, poems, songs, movies, and plays. The tricky aspect of writing titles is not what to capitalize, but what *not* to capitalize. Assess your students' knowledge of this skill by having them copy and correct sentences such as the ones below.

- Charles Dickens wrote ***a tale of two cities***. (book title)
- Have you read the chapter of our history text titled "**the rise and fall of communism**"? (chapter title)
- The title of my story is "**a day to remember**." (story title)
- The article "**computers at home**" ran in the ***washington post***. (title of an article; title of a newspaper)
- Dad subscribes to the magazine ***living with nature***.
- My sister wrote a poem called "**once upon a time**."
- Let's sing "**pop goes the weasel**." (song title)
- Our family watched the movie ***to kill a mockingbird***. (movie title)
- The play was titled ***visitors from an earlier time***. (title of play)

STEP 2:
Pre-test and Grouping for Instruction

Following the introduction, give all students the written pre-test (page 66). Record (or have students record) their scores on an individual record sheet (page 95). Sort through the record sheets and remove the tests of students who scored 100%. You may choose to give these students the post-test right away to verify mastery or wait to give it to them with the rest of the class. Form a group of students who scored 80% or lower for direct instruction and practice.

STEP 3:
Instruction

Present students with the capitalization guideline below. (If you are using the "Practice With a Purpose" coordinated mini-charts, use the rule page with this lesson.) Then correct together the sentences used in the motivational activity. Discuss not only which words in each title are capitalized, but also which are not, and ask students to explain why.

RULE 1 **Capitalize the first, last, and all important words in a title.**

NOTE: Capitalize <u>all</u> nouns and verbs and words of four or more letters.
(The four-letter guide is just one of several acceptable variations in style. It is suggested here because it is simple and easy to remember.)

Words such as *a, an, the, and, of, to in, by,* and *for* are only capitalized if used as the first or last word of a title.

- **Sponges <u>Are</u> Animals!** (*Are* is capitalized because it is a verb.)
- **<u>The</u> Once and Future King** (*The* is capitalized because it is the first word.)
- **Walk <u>With</u> the Dinosaurs** (*With* is capitalized because it has four letters.)

✓ Charles Dickens wrote *<u>A</u> <u>T</u>ale of <u>T</u>wo <u>C</u>ities*.
✓ Have you read the chapter of our history text titled "*<u>T</u>he <u>R</u>ise and <u>F</u>all of <u>C</u>ommunism*"?
✓ The title of my story is "*<u>A</u> <u>D</u>ay to <u>R</u>emember*."
✓ The article "*<u>C</u>omputers at <u>H</u>ome*" ran in the *<u>W</u>ashington <u>P</u>ost.*
✓ Dad subscribes to the magazine *<u>L</u>iving <u>W</u>ith <u>N</u>ature*.
✓ My sister wrote a poem called "*<u>O</u>nce <u>U</u>pon a <u>T</u>ime*."
✓ Let's sing "*<u>P</u>op <u>G</u>oes the <u>W</u>easel*."
✓ Our family watched the movie *<u>T</u>o <u>K</u>ill a <u>M</u>ockingbird*.
✓ The play was titled *<u>V</u>isitors <u>F</u>rom an <u>E</u>arlier <u>T</u>ime*.

STEP 4:
Apply and Practice

Following direct instruction, give students the opportunity to apply the skill in practice. You may use the prepared practice sheet provided (page 65), side two of the "Practice With a Purpose" mini-chart (page 92), or your own practice sentences. Students can use plain writing paper to copy and correct sentences you write on the board or those provided on the mini-chart. If you choose to use the reproducible practice sheet, duplicate only the number needed for your instructional group. (Wait for the pre-test results to determine the exact number of students who will need practice.)

Practice may be guided or done independently. Students may work individually, in pairs, or as a group. Correct the page together or privately to assess the need for reteaching before giving the post-test.

STEP 5:
Post-test and Reteaching

When your students have had sufficient instruction and practice, give the post-test. After recording scores on the individual record sheets, once again separate the sheets of those students who scored 80% or less on the post-test for reteaching. You may use or reuse any of the materials suggested in Step 4 for reteaching.

Follow-up / Enrichment

Once students have mastered the skill, make certain they retain it by giving a follow-up activity several weeks later. An excellent way to do this is to see if they can apply the skill in context. To check for retention, copy the list of Newbery Award Winners onto chart paper. Have students write the list correctly capitalized. Or, if you prefer, use the prepared reproducible activity sheet on the following page. **Tip!** Invite students who have read any of these books to tell the group about them. Then ask students to select a title to read on their own or for you to read aloud.

To be corrected

**Correctly copy this list of
Newbery Award Winners.**

1954 *. . . and now miguel* by Joseph Krumgold

1959 *the witch of blackbird pond* by Elizabeth George Speare

1963 *a wrinkle in time* by Madeleine L'Engle

1973 *julie of the wolves* by Jean C. George

1978 *bridge to terabithia* by Katherine Paterson

1986 *sara, plain and tall* by Sid Fleischman

Corrected

**Answers
(titles only)**

1954 *. . . And Now Miguel*

1959 *The Witch of Blackbird Pond*

1963 *A Wrinkle in Time*

1973 *Julie of the Wolves*

1978 *Bridge to Terabithia*

1986 *Sara, Plain and Tall*

ANSWER KEYS

Pre-test:

1. B)
2. A)
3. B)
4. A)
5. B)

Practice:

1. B)
2. A)
3. A)
4. B)
5. A)

6. B)
7. A)
8. B)
9. B)
10. A)

Post-test:

1. B)
2. A)
3. A)
4. A)
5. B)

**Practice With a Purpose—
Titles of Works**

1. "There's a Hole in the Bucket"
2. *The Day the Earth Stood Still*
3. *The Old Man and the Sea*

4. "A Team to Cheer"
   Grant School Gazette
5. "A Look at Mollusks"

Titles of Works

The Newbery Medal is awarded each year to the author of the most distinguished contribution to children's literature. Correctly copy each award-winning title below.

1954   *. . . and now miguel* by Joseph Krumgold
1959   *the witch of blackbird pond* by Elizabeth George Speare
1963   *a wrinkle in time* by Madeleine L'Engle
1973   *julie of the wolves* by Jean C. George
1978   *bridge to terabithia* by Katherine Paterson
1986   *sara, plain and tall* by Sid Fleischman

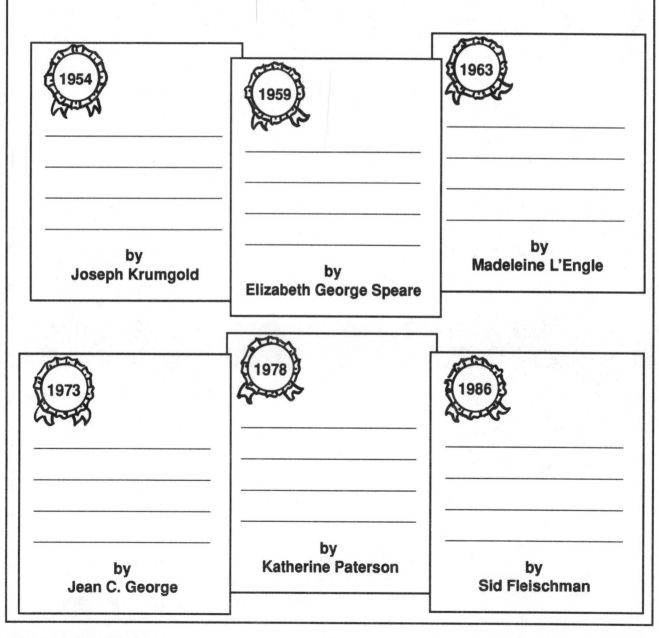

1954
_____
_____
_____
_____
by
Joseph Krumgold

1959
_____
_____
_____
_____
by
Elizabeth George Speare

1963
_____
_____
_____
by
Madeleine L'Engle

1973
_____
_____
_____
by
Jean C. George

1978
_____
_____
_____
_____
by
Katherine Paterson

1986
_____
_____
_____
by
Sid Fleischman

Name _____ Date _____ Score _____

Titles of Works

Directions: Below are the authors and titles of 10 popular books. Choose the letter of the title that shows the correct capitalization.

_____ 1. Frank Baum
    A) *the Wizard of Oz*   B) *The Wizard of Oz*

_____ 2. Anne Frank
    A) *The Diary of a Young Girl*   B) *The Diary Of a Young Girl*

_____ 3. Kenneth Grahame
    A) *The Wind in the Willows*   B) *The wind in the Willows*

_____ 4. Robert Louis Stevenson
    A) *Treasure island*   B) *Treasure Island*

_____ 5. Jonathan Swift
    A) *Gulliver's Travels*   B) *Gulliver's travels*

_____ 6. J. R. R. Tolkien
    A) *the Hobbit*   B) *The Hobbit*

_____ 7. Sheila Burnford
    A) *The Incredible Journey*   B) *The incredible Journey*

_____ 8. Daniel Defoe
    A) *Robinson crusoe*   B) *Robinson Crusoe*

_____ 9. Virginia Hamilton
    A) *The House Of Dies Drear*   B) *The House of Dies Drear*

_____ 10. Mark Twain
    A) *The Adventures of Tom Sawyer*
    B) *the Adventures Of Tom Sawyer*

FS-10172 Plain English—Capitalization

Name _____ Date _____ Score _____

Titles of Works

Directions: A title is missing in each sentence. Write the letter of the title that shows the correct capitalization.

_____ 1. The movie ____ is a Disney classic.
    A) *Lady And The Tramp*   B) *Lady and the Tramp*

_____ 2. Clement Moore's story-poem, ____, is enjoyed by all ages.
    A) "The Night Before Christmas"   B) "The Night before Christmas"

_____ 3. The ____ is a newspaper of special interest to investors.
    A) *Wall street Journal*   B) *Wall Street Journal*

_____ 4. ____ is one of Edgar Allan Poe's most famous stories.
    A) "The Fall of the House of Usher"   B) "The Fall Of The House Of Usher"

_____ 5. Maurice Sendak's ____ is a delightfully scary children's book.
    A) *Where the Wild Things are*   B) *Where the Wild Things Are*

Name _____ Date _____ Score _____

Titles of Works

Directions: A title is missing in each sentence. Write the letter of the title that shows the correct capitalization.

_____ 1. The school play was titled ____ .
    A) *The Gift Of Life*   B) *The Gift of Life*

_____ 2. My story, ____ , won second place in the contest.
    A) "One of a Kind"   B) "One Of a Kind"

_____ 3. ____ by Beverly Cleary is a popular children's book.
    A) *The Mouse and the Motorcycle*   B) *The Mouse And the Motorcycle*

_____ 4. ____ was the most interesting chapter in the history book.
    A) "The Rise and Fall of Rome"   B) "The Rise And Fall Of Rome"

_____ 5. ____ is one of my favorite poems.
    A) "A Walk In My Shoes"   B) "A Walk in My Shoes"

Related materials for teaching Capitalization: Calendar Items
Reproducible: Pre-test and Post-test (page 72); Practice Page (page 71)
Enrichment Activity (page 70)
Rule Book Template (page 6); Individual Record Sheet (page 95)
"Practice With a Purpose": Calendar Items (pages 93-94)

Capitalization: Calendar Items

The ideas on these three pages follow the flow chart of suggested steps for teaching, reteaching, and testing presented on page 3 of this book.

STEP 1:
Motivation—Days, Dates, and Scheduled Events

Introduce the skill by writing several sentences containing references to days of the week, months of the year, holidays, and scheduled events. Ask students to identify the calendar-related item in each sentence and to suggest how it should be written. Here are some sentences:

- If **monday** is a fun day, is **tuesday** just a blues day?
- Thirty days hath **september**, **april**, **june**, and **november**.
- Both **halloween** and **thanksgiving** occur in the fall months.
- Plant a tree on **arbor day**.
- On the fifth of **may**, many Mexican Americans celebrate **cinco de mayo**.
- A religious holiday observed by Jews is **yom kippur**.
- Flyers were sent out announcing activities for **fire prevention week**.
- It is common to display the flag on **june** 14, **flag day**.
- The **academy awards** are viewed annually by millions of movie fans.
- Thousands of people participate each year in the **boston marathon**.

STEP 2:
Pre-test and Grouping for Instruction

Follow the oral introduction above by giving all students the written pre-test (page 72). Record (or have students record) their scores on an individual record sheet (page 95). Sort through the record sheets and remove the tests of students who scored 100%. You may choose to give these students the post-test right away to verify mastery or wait to give it to them with the rest of the class. Form a group of students who scored 80% or lower for direct instruction and practice.

STEP 3:
Instruction

Present students with the sentences used in the motivational activity or other examples with similar references to various days, dates, and events. Offer the rules on the next page as general guidelines for capitalizing calendar items and then correct the sentences together. (If you are using the "Practice With a Purpose" coordinated mini-charts, use the rule page with this lesson.)

RULE 1 **Capitalize days of the week, months of the year, holidays, and special days.**

- Today is Sunday, May 7.
- It is Mother's Day.

RULE 2 **Capitalize the names of calendar events.**

- It is the first day of Be Kind to Animals Week.*

Note that in longer names, capitalization rules are the same as those for titles: Capitalize the first, last, and all important words.

Days of the Week

Sunday	Thursday
Monday	Friday
Tuesday	Saturday
Wednesday	

Months of the Year

January	July
February	August
March	September
April	October
May	November
June	December

Holidays

New Year's Day	Father's Day
Presidents' Day	Fourth of July
Valentine's Day	Halloween
Easter	Thanksgiving
Mother's Day	Hannukah
Flag Day	Christmas

Calendar Events

National Women's History Month
Bicycle Safety Week
Cultural Awareness Fair
Annual Food Drive
Senior Prom
Super Bowl Sunday

STEP 4:
Apply and Practice

Following direct instruction, give students the opportunity to apply the skill in practice. You may use the prepared practice sheet provided (page 71), side two of the "Practice With a Purpose" mini-chart (page 94), or your own practice sentences. Students can use plain writing paper to copy and correct sentences you write on the board or those provided on the mini-chart. If you choose to use the reproducible practice sheet, duplicate only the number needed for your instructional group. (Wait for the pre-test results to determine the exact number of students who will need practice.)

Practice may be guided or done independently. Students may work individually, in pairs, or as a group. Correct the page together or privately to assess the need for reteaching before giving post-test.

STEP 5:
Post-test and Reteaching

When your students have had sufficient instruction and practice, give the post-test. After recording scores on the individual record sheets, once again separate the sheets of those students who scored 80% or less on the post-test for reteaching. You may use or reuse any of the materials suggested in Step 4 for reteaching.

Follow-up / Enrichment

Once students have mastered the skill, make certain they retain it by giving a follow-up activity several weeks later. An excellent way to do this is to see if they can apply the skill in context. Below are directions for an activity you can copy onto chart paper to check for retention. Or, if you prefer, use the prepared reproducible activity sheet on the following page. **Tip!** After students complete the activity, have them trade papers to proofread their responses.

To be completed

Completed

Directions: Copy and complete each sentence.

1. My birthdate is ___.
2. My favorite day of the week is ____.
3. The month I like best is ___ because ___.
4. My favorite holiday is ___. I enjoy it because ___.
5. A holiday I do not celebrate is ___.
6. A school or community event I once attended is ___.
7. An event I am looking forward to is ___.
8. There should be a special day to celebrate ___. I would call it ___.

Students' answers will vary, but must show correct capitalization of days of the week, months of the year, holidays, special days, and calendar events.

ANSWER KEYS

Pre-test:

1. B)	4. B)
2. A)	5. B)
3. B)	

Practice:

1. B)	5. A)	9. B)
2. A)	6. B)	10. C)
3. B)	7. A)	
4. B)	8. C)	

Post-test:

1. C)	4. B)
2. A)	5. C)
3. A)	

Practice With a Purpose— Calendar Items

1. Saturday, July 1; (message correct as is)
2. Sunday, July 2; . . . Scout Round-up Day
3. Monday, July 3; (message correct as is)
4. Tuesday, July 4; Fourth of July; . . . Independence Day Parade
5. Wednesday, July 5; . . . Bugged-About-Litter Week

Name_____ Date_____

Calendar Items

Complete the statements. Use the capitalization rules you have learned. Illustrate one of the statements in the frame.

(1) My birthdate is _____.

(2) My favorite day of the week is _____.

(3) The month I like best is _____ because _____

_____.

(4) My favorite holiday is _____. I enjoy it because

_____.

(5) A holiday I do not celebrate is _____.

(6) A school or community event I once

attended is _____

_____.

(7) An event I am looking forward to is

_____

_____.

(8) There should be a special day to

celebrate _____

_____.

I would call it _____

_____.

Calendar Items

Directions: Find the capitalization error in each sentence. Write *A*, *B*, or *C* to indicate the correction that is needed.

All Through the Year

_____ 1. Begin the year with New Year's day—a fun and happy holiday.
A) new   B) Day   C) Holiday

_____ 2. Come february it is time to send your sweetheart a valentine.
A) February   B) Sweetheart   C) Valentine

_____ 3. All through March we celebrate National women's History Month.
A) march   B) Women's   C) month

_____ 4. April showers bring may flowers—and the start of spring!
A) april   B) May   C) Spring

_____ 5. The second monday in June begins National Little League Baseball Week.
A) Monday   B) june   C) little

_____ 6. It is the Fourth Of July! Let the fireworks begin!
A) fourth   B) of   C) Fireworks

_____ 7. No holidays in august? Why not celebrate National Aviation Day?
A) August   B) aviation   C) day

_____ 8. September and October—have your own Johnny Appleseed festival.
A) september   B) october   C) Festival

_____ 9. On the fourth thursday in November, give thanks for all you have.
A) Fourth   B) Thursday   C) november

_____ 10. Want to do something different in December? Celebrate Aardvark week!
A) december   B) aardvark   C) Week

Bonus! Write and illustrate a month-by-month calendar highlighting one or more special things you especially look forward to each month.

Name _____ **Date** _____ **Score** _____

Calendar Items

Directions: Write *A* if the sentence is capitalized correctly. Write *B* or *C* if the change indicated is needed.

_____ 1. Today is wednesday, May 17.
   A) correct   B) Wednesday   C) may

_____ 2. It is Children's Book Week.
   A) correct   B) book C) week

_____ 3. Valentine's day is February 14.
   A) correct   B) Day   C) february

_____ 4. Monday begins Plant A Tree Week.
   A) correct   B) a   C) tree

_____ 5. Let's have a picnic on flag Day.
   A) correct   B) Flag   C) day

Name _____ **Date** _____ **Score** _____

Calendar Items

Directions: Write *A* if the sentence is capitalized correctly. Write *B* or *C* if the change indicated is needed.

_____ 1. It is almost October 31—halloween!
   A) correct   B) october   C) Halloween

_____ 2. Melissa's party is on Saturday night.
   A) correct   B) saturday   C) Night

_____ 3. The Festival of Lights will be held soon.
   A) correct   B) Of   C) lights

_____ 4. The Vale county Fair is in August each year.
   A) correct   B) County   C) august

_____ 5. We are taking Mom out to dinner on Mother's day.
   A) correct   B) mother's   C) Day

Pronoun—*I*

Instead of My Name

Always capitalize the pronoun *I*.

A pronoun is a word that takes the place of a noun. The word *I* takes the place of your name. Capitalize *I* when it stands alone or is part of a contraction (*I, I'm, I'll, I'd*).

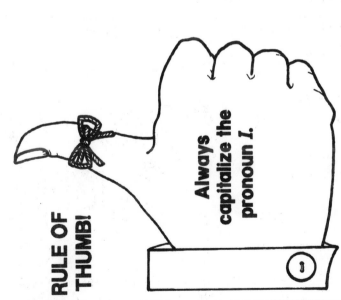

RULE OF THUMB!

Always capitalize the pronoun *I*.

✔ **Today *I* have to give my presentation.**

✔ ***I* am ready, but *I'm* a little nervous.**

✔ ***I'm* afraid that *I'll* forget something.**

✔ **Even though *I* think *I* know it, *I'd* like to be sure.**

✔ **Maybe *I'd* better practice just once more.**

Practice With a Purpose
Rule and Reference

Pronoun—*I*

Pronoun—I

Rewrite the story with correct capitalization.

Go Fish

1. Dad and i like to go fishing.

2. i haven't caught a fish yet.

3. Dad says i need to be patient.

4. If i wait long enough, a fish will bite.

5. When i do catch one, though, i'll throw it back.

✔ Always capitalize the pronoun *I*.

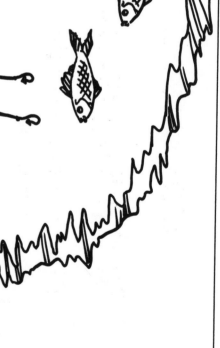

Practice With a Purpose
Follow-up and Practice

Pronoun—*I*

Beginning of a Sentence

In the Beginning

Always capitalize the first word of a sentence.

Every sentence, whether it stands alone or is part of a paragraph, must begin with a capital letter.

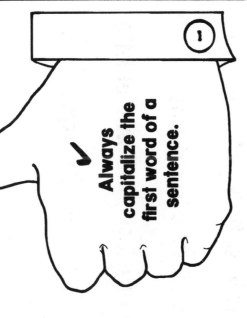

RULE OF THUMB!

Always capitalize the first word of a sentence.

Although they look similar, not all horses are the same. Some breeds of horses are especially well-suited for pleasure riding. The Tennessee Walker is a fine saddle horse. Thoroughbreds are better suited for racing. Draft horses, the biggest and strongest breeds, are most often used for work.

Practice With a Purpose
Rule and Reference

Beginning of a Sentence

 FS-10172 Plain English—Capitalization

Beginning of a Sentence

Copy the paragraph, filling in the missing letter at the beginning of each sentence.

Always capitalize the first word of a sentence.

( )ow do desert animals go so long without a drink? ( )he plant-eaters get water from grasses and leaves. ( )eat-eaters get fluids from the bodies of the animals and insects they eat. ( )esert-dwelling animals must conserve what little moisture they have. ( )any hide in dens or burrows during the heat of day and come out at night to hunt for food.

Practice With a Purpose
Follow-up and Practice

Beginning of a Sentence

FS-10172 Plain English—Capitalization

Beginning of a Quote

You Can Quote Me

Capitalize the first word of a sentence in a direct quote.

HINT! Think of quotes as separate, complete sentences. If a quoted sentence is begun, interrupted, then continues, capitalize the beginning of the quote but not the fragment that completes the sentence.

✓ Mary asked, "_Where is Denmark?_"
(Quote is a complete sentence.)

✓ "_Denmark,_" replied Ryan, "_is in Europe._"
(Quoted sentence is interrupted.)

✓ "_I know something else about Denmark,_" said Jeff. "_The capital is Copenhagen._"
(Each quote is a complete sentence.)

RULE OF THUMB!

Capitalize the first word of a sentence in a direct quote.

①

Practice With a Purpose
Rule and Reference

Beginning of a Quote

Beginning of a Quote

Write each sentence. Correct all capitalization errors.

Oh, Deer

(1) "did you know," said Manuel, "that there are more than 600 kinds of deer?"

(2) Steve replied, "when I think of deer, I picture only white-tailed deer."

(3) "actually, caribou and elk are deer," said Manuel. "even moose are in the deer family!"

(4) Steve thought for a moment and then said, "what other animal could be a type of deer?"

(5) The boys looked at each other and laughed, "what about reindeer?"

Capitalize the first word of a sentence in a direct quote.

People / Animals

Mentioned by Name

Capitalize names and initials of people.
Capitalize names of pets and animal characters.

HINT! Names of specific people (*Dave, Mom*) and specific animal names (*Spot, Flipper*) are capitalized. General names (*a boy, my mother, the dog*) are not.

Study the examples below.
Specific names are capitalized.
General names are not capitalized.

✔ My name is *Jim Gibbs*.

✔ I have a *sister* named *Kathy*.

✔ My *mother*, *Jean*, is a *veterinarian*.

✔ We have two *pets*—a *dog* named *Max* and a *cat* named *Squeaky*.

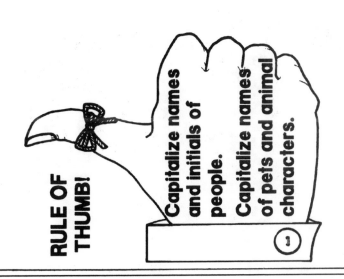

RULE OF THUMB!

Capitalize names and initials of people.

Capitalize names of pets and animal characters.

①

Practice With a Purpose
Follow-up and Practice

People / Animals

79

People / Animals

Correct the errors in capitalization as you copy each sentence. Then write the title of the book described.

Capitalize names and initials of people. Capitalize names of pets and animal characters.

Some Pig

1. It is a famous book by e. b. white.

2. The star is a pig named wilbur.

3. One of his friends is a girl named fern.

4. He also knows templeton, a rat.

5. But wilbur's best friend is a special spider called charlotte.

Places / Locations

Where It Is

Capitalize the names of specific places and locations.

- **continents, countries, states, cities**
  - ✔ <u>L</u>ondon, <u>E</u>ngland

- **islands, mountains**
  - ✔ <u>H</u>awaiian <u>I</u>slands

- **oceans, lakes, rivers**
  - ✔ <u>L</u>ake <u>S</u>uperior

- **parks, forests, canyons**
  - ✔ <u>Y</u>osemite <u>N</u>ational <u>P</u>ark

- **street names**
  - ✔ <u>C</u>edar <u>L</u>ane

RULE OF THUMB!

Capitalize the names of specific places and locations.

NOTE!

Capitalize direction words only when they refer to a section of the country or world or when they are part of a place name.

- ✔ the <u>F</u>ar <u>E</u>ast
- ✔ <u>S</u>outh <u>O</u>ak <u>D</u>rive

Practice With a Purpose
Rule and Reference

Places / Locations

Places / Locations

Copy the sentences. Capitalize specific place names.

✔ Capitalize the names of specific places and locations.

(1) Our exchange student from asia tells us about her homeland, japan. (2) Her home is on ginza avenue in the capital city of tokyo. (3) She describes japan as a group of main islands, the largest of which is honshu. (4) But she says that west of honshu, in inland sea, there are over 1,000 tiny wooded islands. (5) Still, her favorite description is that of the beauty of mt. fuji, an ancient volcano.

Practice With a Purpose
Follow-up and Practice

Places / Locations

82   FS-10172 Plain English—Capitalization

Special Things

Specifically Speaking

Capitalize the names of specific ships, aircraft and spacecraft, works of art, celestial bodies, buildings, monuments, and landmarks.

Capitalize the names of specific ships, aircraft and spacecraft, works of art, celestial bodies, buildings, monuments, and landmarks.

- specific ships
  ✔ *Titantic*

- specific aircraft / spacecraft
  ✔ *Hindenburg; Apollo II*

- specific works of art
  ✔ Michelangelo's *David*

- specific celestial bodies
  ✔ Jupiter; North Star

- specific buildings
  ✔ Eiffel Tower

- specific monuments
  ✔ Jefferson Memorial

- specific landmarks
  ✔ Stonehenge

Practice With a Purpose
Rule and Reference

Special Things

Special Things

Match each description with the name of the special thing described. Capitalize as needed.

Capitalize the names of ships, aircraft and spacecraft, works of art, celestial bodies, buildings, monuments, and landmarks.

- *nautilus*
- parthenon
- lincoln memorial
- saturn
- *the starry night*

(1) The planet known for its colorful rings:

(2) A famous painting by Vincent van Gogh:

(3) An ancient Greek temple:

(4) The submarine that sailed under the North Pole:

(5) A monument to the sixteenth president:

Practice With a Purpose
Follow-up and Practice

Special Things

© Frank Schaffer Publications, Inc.

FS-10172 Plain English—Capitalization

Groups / Languages

① Strength in Numbers

Capitalize names of specific groups.

- nations, nationalities, cultures
  - ✓ <u>V</u>ietnam, <u>V</u>ietnamese
- religions, religious groups
  - ✓ <u>I</u>slam, <u>I</u>slamic
- agencies, organizations, clubs
  - ✓ <u>S</u>tate <u>D</u>epartment
  - ✓ <u>B</u>oy <u>S</u>couts of <u>A</u>merica
- companies, businesses, schools
  - ✓ <u>S</u>mith's <u>G</u>rocery <u>S</u>tore
  - ✓ <u>K</u>ennedy <u>H</u>igh <u>S</u>chool

② In Any Language

Capitalize names of languages.

- ✓ <u>S</u>panish, <u>E</u>nglish, <u>R</u>ussian, <u>H</u>ebrew

RULE OF THUMB! ①
Capitalize names of specific groups.

RULE OF THUMB! ②
Capitalize names of languages.

Practice With a Purpose
Rule and Reference

Groups / Languages

© Frank Schaffer Publications, Inc.   85   FS-10172 Plain English—Capitalization

Groups / Languages

Match each description with the specific group or language described. Capitalize as needed.

(1) A government agency that studies population:

(2) The language of the Netherlands:

(3) An affiliation of sports teams:

(4) The oldest college in America:

(5) The native inhabitants of Australia:

- dutch
- harvard
- aborigines
- census bureau
- national football league

✓ Capitalize names of specific groups.
✓ Capitalize names of languages.

Practice With a Purpose

Follow-up and Practice

Groups / Languages

Events / Documents

① Historical Times

Capitalize names of specific events and time periods.

✔ Trojan War
✔ Crusades
✔ Industrial Revolution
✔ Cuban Missile Crisis
✔ Ice Age

Capitalize names of specific events and time periods.

② Historical Actions

Capitalize names of specific documents, declarations, and acts.

✔ Monroe Doctrine
✔ Emancipation Proclamation
✔ Sugar Act

Capitalize names of specific documents, declarations, and acts.

RULE OF THUMB!

Capitalize names of specific documents, declarations, and acts.

Practice With a Purpose
Rule and Reference

Events / Documents

Events / Documents

Write the sentences in chronological order. Capitalize as needed.

✓ Capitalize names of specific events and time periods.

✓ Capitalize names of specific documents, declarations, and acts.

- In 1815 the french revolution ended at the battle of waterloo.

- Europe's dark ages began with the fall of Rome in 476 and lasted for 300 years.

- In 1215 English nobles presented the king with a list of 63 demands known as the magna carta.

- American colonists protested British taxes by staging the boston tea party in 1774.

- The roaring twenties was a period of prosperity early in this century.

Practice With a Purpose
Follow-up and Practice

Events / Documents

Titles of Respect

Special Identification

Capitalize the title of a person when it is part of, or takes the place of, the person's name.

✔ Our <u>coach</u>, Jim Post, began to speak. *(not part of a name)*

✔ "Are you ready?" asked <u>Coach</u> Post. *(part of a name)*

✔ "We are ready, <u>Coach</u>," we shouted. *(replaces a name)*

NOTE! Capitalize abbreviations of titles, too.

✔	✔
<u>Mrs.</u> Kane	<u>U</u>ncle Max
<u>Mr.</u> Rosen	<u>A</u>unt Jean
<u>Gov.</u> Brown	<u>J</u>udge Marshall
Joe Kim, <u>Jr.</u>	<u>P</u>resident Clinton
<u>Dr.</u> Diaz	<u>M</u>other Teresa
<u>General</u> Grant	F. Mills, <u>M. D.</u>
<u>C</u>aptain Hook	<u>Col.</u> Powell
Lisa Ian, <u>Ph. D.</u>	<u>Rev.</u> Jackson

RULE OF THUMB!

Capitalize the title of a person when it is part of, or takes the place of, the person's name.

Practice With a Purpose
Rule and Reference

Titles of Respect

FS-10172 Plain English—Capitalization

Titles of Respect

Capitalize the title of a person when it is part of, or takes the place of, the person's name.

Write each sentence. Capitalize as needed.

1. It was a proud day for dr. and mrs. Thomas.

2. Their son, Marcus, jr., was graduating from the Taft Police Academy.

3. Marcus's uncle, a police lieutenant, was also there.

4. Marcus beamed as he accepted the certificate from the captain.

5. "Congratulations, officer Thomas," said Capt. Cole with a smile.

Practice With a Purpose
Follow-up and Practice

Titles of Respect

FS-10172 Plain English—Capitalization

Titles of Works

A Matter of Importance

Capitalize the first, last, and all important words in a title.

NOTE! Capitalize *all* nouns and verbs and words of four or more letters.

Words such as *a, an, the, and, of, to, in, by,* and *for* are only capitalized if used as the first or last word of a title.

✔ *The Flowers of Holland* (book)

✔ "That Was the Day" (story)

✔ "Animal Habitats" (chapter)

✔ "Pie in the Sky" (song)

✔ "A View From the Top" (article)

✔ *Town and Country Gazette* (newspaper)

✔ "Leaves of Autumn" (poem)

RULE OF THUMB!

Capitalize the first, last, and all important words in a title.

Titles of Works

Rewrite each sentence capitalized correctly.

(1) I know all the verses to the song "there's a hole in the bucket."

(2) My favorite science fiction movie is *the day the earth stood still.*

3) Ernest Hemingway's book *the old man and the sea* is a classic.

(4) I wrote the article "a team to cheer" for the *grant school gazette,* our school newspaper.

(5) Read the chapter titled "a look at mollusks" in your science book.

There's a hole in the bucket, dear Liza, dear Liza!

Capitalize the first, last, and all important words in a title.

Practice With a Purpose
Follow-up and Practice

Titles of Works

FS-10172 Plain English—Capitalization

Calendar Items

It's a Date!

① **Capitalize days of the week, months of the year, holidays, and special days.**

Capitalize days of the week, months of the year, holidays, and special days.

✔ My birthday is <u>J</u>une 18.
✔ The party will be on <u>S</u>aturday.
✔ I was born on <u>F</u>ather's <u>D</u>ay.

② **Capitalize the names of calendar events.**

Capitalize the names of calendar events.

✔ <u>S</u>uper <u>B</u>owl <u>S</u>unday is in January.
✔ February is <u>B</u>lack <u>H</u>istory <u>M</u>onth.
✔ The <u>S</u>cience <u>F</u>air will be held in April.
✔ The fire department will hold its annual <u>T</u>oys for <u>T</u>ots drive in December.

Practice With a Purpose
Rule and Reference

Calendar Items

Calendar Items

Rewrite Lee's reminder notes capitalized correctly.

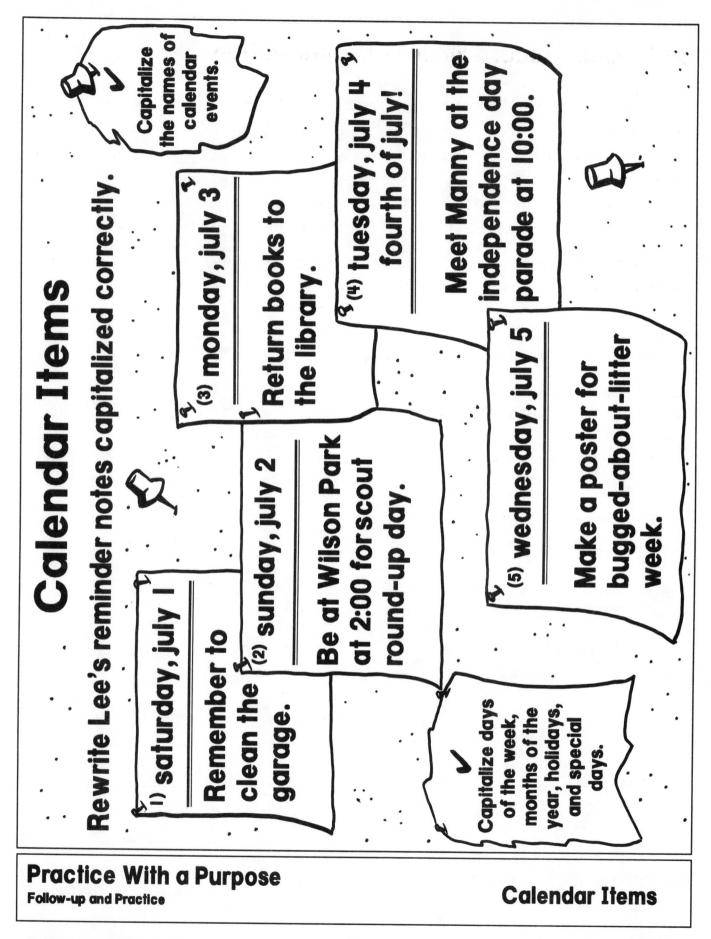

Capitalize the names of calendar events.

Capitalize days of the week, months of the year, holidays, and special days.

1) saturday, july 1
Remember to clean the garage.

(2) sunday, july 2
Be at Wilson Park at 2:00 for scout round-up day.

(3) monday, july 3
Return books to the library.

(4) tuesday, july 4
fourth of july!
Meet Manny at the independence day parade at 10:00.

(5) wednesday, july 5
Make a poster for bugged-about-litter week.

Practice With a Purpose
Follow-up and Practice

Calendar Items

94

FS-10172 Plain English—Capitalization

Individual Record Sheet—Capitalization

Name _____ Date begun _____ Student # _____

1. Pronoun—I

# correct		20%		40%		60%		80%		100%	
Pre-test	0	1		2		3		4		5	
Practice	0	1	2	3	4	5	6	7	8	9	10
Post-test	0	1		2		3		4		5	

2. Beginning of a Sentence

# correct		20%		40%		60%		80%		100%	
Pre-test	0	1		2		3		4		5	
Practice	0	1	2	3	4	5	6	7	8	9	10
Post-test	0	1		2		3		4		5	

3. Beginning of a Quote

# correct		20%		40%		60%		80%		100%	
Pre-test	0	1		2		3		4		5	
Practice	0	1	2	3	4	5	6	7	8	9	10
Post-test	0	1		2		3		4		5	

4. People / Animals

# correct		20%		40%		60%		80%		100%	
Pre-test	0	1		2		3		4		5	
Practice	0	1	2	3	4	5	6	7	8	9	10
Post-test	0	1		2		3		4		5	

5. Places / Locations

# correct		20%		40%		60%		80%		100%	
Pre-test	0	1		2		3		4		5	
Practice	0	1	2	3	4	5	6	7	8	9	10
Post-test	0	1		2		3		4		5	

6. Special Things

# correct		20%		40%		60%		80%		100%	
Pre-test	0	1		2		3		4		5	
Practice	0	1	2	3	4	5	6	7	8	9	10
Post-test	0	1		2		3		4		5	

7. Groups / Languages

# correct		20%		40%		60%		80%		100%	
Pre-test	0	1		2		3		4		5	
Practice	0	1	2	3	4	5	6	7	8	9	10
Post-test	0	1		2		3		4		5	

8. Events / Documents

# correct		20%		40%		60%		80%		100%	
Pre-test	0	1		2		3		4		5	
Practice	0	1	2	3	4	5	6	7	8	9	10
Post-test	0	1		2		3		4		5	

9. Titles of Respect

# correct		20%		40%		60%		80%		100%	
Pre-test	0	1		2		3		4		5	
Practice	0	1	2	3	4	5	6	7	8	9	10
Post-test	0	1		2		3		4		5	

10. Titles of Works

# correct		20%		40%		60%		80%		100%	
Pre-test	0	1		2		3		4		5	
Practice	0	1	2	3	4	5	6	7	8	9	10
Post-test	0	1		2		3		4		5	

11. Calendar Items

# correct		20%		40%		60%		80%		100%	
Pre-test	0	1		2		3		4		5	
Practice	0	1	2	3	4	5	6	7	8	9	10
Post-test	0	1		2		3		4		5	

UNIT TEST—Capitalization

# correct		20%		40%		60%		80%		100%	
Test	0	1	2	3	4	5	6	7	8	9	10

Name _____ Date _____ Score _____

Capitalization Checkup

Read the story. Find 10 places in which the capitalization is incorrect.
Rewrite the story correctly on the lines below. Circle the changes you made.

William Shakespeare

William shakespeare is one of the greatest poets and dramatists to write in the english language. even those who have never read such works as *Romeo And Juliet* or *Hamlet* are familiar with quotes from Shakespeare's writings. Who has not heard "to be or not to be—that is the question"?

Shakespeare was born in april 1564. The family home still stands on Henley street in Stratford-on-Avon, England.

Shakespeare's writings reflect the beliefs and conditions of Englishmen under the rule of queen Elizabeth I. This period known as the Elizabethan age, was one of expansion in both ideas and exploration. Although playhouses, such as the globe, first appeared in Shakespeare's time, all of the parts, male and female, were played by males.

_____
_____
_____
_____
_____
_____
_____
_____
_____
_____
_____
_____
_____
_____
_____
_____
_____

ANSWERS—*FOLD UNDER BEFORE DUPLICATING:* 1. Shakespeare   2. English   3. Even   4. *Romeo and Juliet*   5. To be . . .
6. April   7. Henley Street   8. Queen Elizabeth   9. Elizabethan Age   10. Globe